Lela

Ashes of Childhood

Namuli Hutchinson Books

Published by Namuli Hutchinson Books.

1ˢᵗ edition published June 2019 in Great Britain.

ISBN - 978-1-5272-4273-9

We dedicate this book to future generations. To those that cannot believe in a life that is better. Reclaim *your* story, you are not alone, the horizon will be brighter.

And to our own future generation – Z,A,X-E, S&O, with love always xx

Foreword

By Jon Uglow of the Rafiki Thabo Foundation

The Lela I met back in 2006 danced in the kitchen, sulked in her bedroom and had a wardrobe heaving with clothes, much like any other teenager in the UK. I can't quite remember our very first introduction, but Lela has been part of the fabric of family life for many years, even though in the early days she was still schooling in Uganda, so only around during the long summer recess.

Over the years we and our families have grown very close, our lives inter-twined and linked through weddings, baptisms, crisis' and celebrations. Our children are cousins to each other, allies in the same playground, and yet how different it all could have been.

The context of Lela's childhood in Uganda is not something that I am unfamiliar with – I have spent significant periods of time in rural Kenya, living with families where life was on a knife-edge, reliant on good rains for a plentiful harvest in order to hold together precarious finances. I have seen my friends struggling to educate their children, often making impossible choices about which of them attend school and which must stay at home until more money was available.

What doesn't get spoken of is what happens next; when the crops fail, when there is no money for any school fees. When medical bills suck every last desperate coin and the end of the road is reached. Food is not just basic; it is not there at all. This is where the story often stops: it's not a news-worthy disaster, not a flood or a famine, but it is a point of stark, brutal realities faced by millions. A point where women and children in a patriarchal society find themselves open to merciless exploitation. Mostly, at this point, they, and their life story, are simply ground down and reduced to dust, as if they had never been.

Lela was at that point, but by grace, she came through it and survived. This is her story, the story behind the strong, compassionate, laughter-filled woman I know today. She tells it for herself, for her children, for us who have not been there

5

so that we might see what the reality of life is for so many. Most importantly, she tells her story for all those who didn't get chance to speak for themselves, for those crushed into obscurity by their poverty.

There is no gloss paint thick enough to smooth over the raw struggle for survival and the twisted, brutal exploitation of vulnerability described in this book. I wept my way through the pages, angry at the perpetrators, angry at the world that any young girl, let alone Lela, should have to experience this. Even by telling her story today, Lela stands as a beacon of hope – she has not been defined by the experience of her childhood; in these pages, she redeems it for herself.

As well as giving a voice to the oppressed, Lela has chosen that every purchase of this book will serve to extend hope to others who today find themselves in situations not dissimilar to that of her childhood. Through donating a percentage of the sales profit to the UK registered charity Rafiki Thabo Foundation, 'Lela, Ashes of a Childhood' will contribute towards transforming the lives of young people in Uganda, Kenya and Lesotho, enabling those without financial means to access education. With education comes opportunity for employment, empowerment to navigate out of poverty and most importantly hope for a better tomorrow.

I am privileged indeed to know Lela and thank her for her bravery in telling this story.

"Memories demand attention, because memories have teeth"

Viola Davis

Fairytales bring stories of beauty, of life, of joy. For Uganda it is the fertile soils, the lush green land, the wildlife, the staggering sunrises and the joyful, welcoming people. But under the warmest sun there are always shadows. War, HIV, poverty, and the orphans that are left in the wake. I was once one of them, but today, I am Lela, and this is my story.

This book is based on Lela's childhood memories. Because of its sensitivity, names and places have been replaced with pseudonyms; but the incidents and experiences shared are true to memory.

Part One

Ashes of Childhood

Chapter One

The taxi driver puts my small leather suitcase onto the tarmac while Mr. Webb helps move the larger bags out of the boot and pays the driver his due. I wait to one side; fearful the Ugandan dirt will soil my pure white outfit. I have heard the people of England are clean, the land rich, and no one is poor. I wish to fit in, my clothes to be crisp like theirs, to make an impression. As the Webbs arrange their luggage onto a large metal trolley outside the terminal, I take a final glimpse of the land I call home. We are up early, the sun had barely risen when we left for the airport, yet now it hovers above the horizon, the sky burnt orange, silhouetting the storks and cranes as they head to Lake Victoria for their early morning bathe. On the breeze I can smell the scents of the lake. I close my eyes and allow the air to play with the loose strands of my hair, tickling my forehead. I will fix it before we land in the Great Kingdom of Britain. I strain to hear the sounds of the lake, but Entebbe's noise, the traffic, the shouting and the roar from the runway all block out the sound of the wildlife. These are the noises of my childhood, the noises I will cherish forever.

Eight Years Earlier

'Lela, lazy girl, get up, fetch the water.'

I am awake, dressed and ready to leave, but still Maama yells at me. She bustles around the kitchen as she prepares breakfast for the bigger girls. She is not tall, but large-chested, giving off a greater presence. She is dressed in her usual deep purple cotton dress. It reaches her ankles, leaving enough room for her bunioned feet to peep out, tightly strapped to her worn leather sandals. She adjusts the deep yellow scarf tied around her thick black braids before chopping fresh, ripe pineapples, straight from the plantation. My stomach rumbles, but I will not get food until I have returned. It is commonplace for the children around here to fetch water, yet I am the only one to do it in this house, as the bigger children are at school. I know I must help in some way. Today is not a school day, so I hesitate before gathering the jerry cans, wondering if any of the others will join me. Sometimes they do, not to gather water but just for the company, at least for the first mile or so until they become distracted by a game of football or chase. Maama scolds them when they help me. It is not fair, the others do so little. Perhaps it is because I am the youngest.

'Go girl, what do you wait for? You must return before noon; you have washing to do.' My sisters; Josephine, Caroline and Faith, glance sleepily from their food. Josephine, the eldest, so like Maama already, smirks despite her tiredness. Neither Caroline nor Faith are in a rush to join me on my travels either, so I gather up the six jerry cans ready to start the two-mile journey to the pump. Taata passes me as I push my way through the door, still in his striped night shirt and flip flops.

'Be safe, girl' he calls and winks at me.

I glance back with a smile. The day is already hot, and I am hungry, but I prefer the walk to being stuck with Maama all day, scolded and pushed around by her or one of the other kids if they feel like it. I leave the small compound where we live, a group of a few houses sharing a latrine. For the area they are desirable houses; sturdy walls, windows and multiple rooms. I pass a lot worse on my daily walk. As soon as I enter the main street, the hubbub of central Kampala takes over. It is quieter than most days, with many off work for the weekend, yet hordes of people meander along the centre of the road, delaying the traffic. The cars honk and their drivers yell at children playing and heavily pregnant women balancing goods on their well-wound head scarves. The traders have set up already, men and women sitting low to the ground with fruit and vegetables displayed on small tables or lying on sheets on the dusty ground. They call out their prices loudly, hoping to undercut their neighbours. Over the pollution my nostrils snatch scents of mandazi and mputa, only making my stomach rumble more. I hum to myself and attempt to brush off the hunger, waving cheerily to the familiar faces I see every day; the old woman sweeping her porch, the elderly men who play mweso outside a battered looking coffee shop. The friendly faces make the walk bearable.

Saturdays and Sundays are my favourite days to trek to the pump. The children play happily outside their homes. The boys support football teams based a million miles away, many of them wearing shirts embellished with strange sounding names, kicking a ball around and celebrating a score with their shirts over their heads. The girls play at being mothers. Wrapping avocado 'dolls' to their chests. I am a stranger to them, so I am shy about joining in. They know each other from school I suppose, maybe they will know me one day too.

For as long as I can remember my day has been made up of chores, chores, chores. I long to go to school with my siblings and have the chance to learn and to make friends. Taata had mentioned it this week. 'Lela,' he had said, 'Would you like to join your sisters at school?' I had leapt with joy at the prospect, but Maama had scowled. Why was she so opposed? My sisters are always so busy studying for the future, ready to make the family proud, that's what Maama always says, they won't bring the family shame. I want to make my family proud too. I will study hard, finish school, maybe attend college in the city like some of the teenagers do. I will make Maama proud, then she will not scold me so much. I will work hard and send good money home, so she can live in luxury.

I picture my future as I queue for the pump. The line is already long. A small girl attempts to pump the water at the front of the gathering. Her muscles are weak, and a taller boy is forced to help her. He looks irritated, using up his energy when it isn't even his water. When I am grown up, I won't have my children queuing under the hot African sun for a taste of fresh water. Children only have one chance to be children. At last it is my turn. No longer a novice, I fill my jerry cans quickly, to my relief. The sun is growing higher in the sky with every minute that passes and Maama's temper will be growing too. It does not matter how long the water takes, every day the same chores must be completed. I will have clothes to wash, and then I must help bathe the older children. They are allowed to play then, their washing futile as they always return filthier than before. Whilst they play, I must sweep the compound, clean the house, cook the food. I long to have some friends of my own. If I get to go to school too then that shall come in time, won't it?

When I get home, I pull the jerry cans through the door, sweating and grateful to get out of the sun. The rainy season is a long way off. As my eyes adjust, I notice a stranger seated at the table. My sisters regard her with obvious curiosity. It is not unusual to have guests. Every now and then another face appears, a cousin who has been away, neighbours. Kampala may be sprawling but it has never lost its village feel. This face is new.

'Girl, come here, you are late.' Maama is cross, I can tell by her voice, but she will not shout at me in front of this guest. I step away from the jerry cans and approach the table.

'Say hello to your Step Auntie Maria.'

I do as I'm told. Aunt Maria stands and approaches me. She is short like Maama, but more petite in looks, and prettier, her face not yet ravaged by the sun. Her smile is tender, her look, kindly. She reaches out to touch me. I flinch. I'm not used to being touched tenderly.

'Hello Lela. Are you well?'

'Yes, thank you.'

'Maama tells me you wish to start school soon?'

'Yes, I want to make my family proud.'

'You will Lela, you will.' She smiles again, but she looks strained, weary. She touches my shoulder. Her hands are calloused.

'She's so thin,' says Aunt Maria. Maama glares at me, like a volcano about to erupt.

'Leave us now child,' Taata smiles gently at me. I must finish my chores and my siblings are dismissed to play. I sweep the yard, loitering in the shade. I hear raised voices from inside the kitchen. I move my broom cautiously, so it doesn't block out all sound. It is Maama who shouts. I wonder what Aunt Maria has done to make my mother so mad.

14

It is dinner time before I am allowed back in the house. I have cooked a simple Katogo stew on the outside fire, using vegetables and offal bought by Taata this morning. It smells so fresh that I sneak some when I'm sure no one is looking. It is my first food of the day. When inside, I eat hungrily, grateful for our guest. Thanks to her, I have been given more food than usual.

'You see, she eats just fine,' Maama mutters to Maria. The table is quiet now, as soon as dinner is over Maria prepares to head home. She compliments my cooking, then takes me to one side.

'You are a good girl Lela. Keep doing what Maama says, yes?'

'Yes, Aunt Maria.' She ruffles my unkempt hair and kisses my forehead. The only person who ever kisses me is Taata.

Taata whispers that it's time for us girls to go to bed. He squeezes us in a bear hug and kisses us all. Long after we retire to our shared bedroom, I hear Taata telling Maama that it is not my fault. What is not my fault? She shouts that I need to pay my way around here. He says I belong in school. I hope Taata wins this argument.

I cannot sleep with the raised voices. My three sisters are still awake, cosy, side by side in their tall single beds. I lie on a mattress in the far corner. I watch my sisters' feet, three pairs all sticking out of their warm bedclothes. I am chilly under my threadbare sheet. Uganda may be warm in daylight, but at night, sheltered only by bare concrete walls, I shiver. Josephine throws something at me in the darkness.

'You know it is your fault that Maama and Taata fight,' she says.

'Shut up,' I hiss. I know it is true, but I do not wish to hear it.

'They never used to fight until you came along.' She curls back into bed whilst I quiver on my mattress with cold and nervous tension. Under my breath I repeat a rhyme I have heard children saying in the street to stop myself from crying. They are merciless when I cry, especially Josephine. I turn to face the wall. The final sound of flip flops in the hall and a slammed door tells me their battle is over. I hope Taata has won. Still sleep evades me. I trace the cracks in the wall with my finger. I know the cracks well; I've traced them many times. Why is Maama always angry with me? She never hits the others. She is tender with them when they are ill. Why do my sisters hate me? It is an effort to clear my mind but eventually I doze restlessly on my mattress and wake before dawn.

Maama does not want me to go to school as I am too useful at home, but I want to go so badly. If I can please her, she may allow me yet. I concoct a plan to keep her happy, dressing silently in the dark. The others are still deep in sleep. I creep down the hall and prepare the jerry cans. I shall set off as soon as she has woken, so she knows I am not disobeying her and simply running off. At last she staggers wearily into the kitchen. The sight of me sitting on the floor startles her.

'Girl, why do you creep about?'

'Sorry Maama, I am leaving to fetch the water.'

'Well, go.'

She did not scold me. Today will be a good day.

The streets are silent. Not even the youngest children have risen. This bodes well for me finishing long before midday. I keep my head down, avoiding eye contact with the few that are up. A group of men shout and jeer at each other. It seems I am early enough to catch those still up from a night of drinking. One pushes another and the others yell and laugh. These are the men I know I need to avoid. I move into the shadows, still pitch enough to conceal my dark skin, keeping close to the walls so I can scurry, like a cockroach, or a rat. Despite the heavy cans weighing me down on my return, the sun is far from overhead when our little street comes into view. My sisters lean against the outside wall, awaiting my return. They only do this when they are expecting trouble.

'Tut tut, what have you done now?' Josephine says gleefully. My heart is beating so loudly suddenly I can hear it in my chest. How can I be in trouble?

Taata and Maama are seated at the table. The remaining chairs stand empty. I know better than to sit down. I am rarely invited to join them at the table.

'Lela come please.' Taata speaks, but not unkindly. He takes my hand, still sweaty from the jerry cans. He wipes my palms on the fabric of his trousers.

'You work hard, my child.' I nod. I see Maama roll her eyes. 'Lela, I know you want to go to school.'

My eyes dart from him to Maama and back again. Am I to be allowed, finally, to attend school with my siblings?

'Yes, Taata.'

'Then you shall go, my dear.'

'Taata thank you, thank you, I shall make you so proud.'

'You will my child, you will.' I throw my arms around his neck and see that behind his back, Maama is pretending to gag.

She rises from the table, slowly, her heavy chest weighing her down and noisily arranges the utensils in the kitchen. I'm so excited that I don't mind her anger.

'Taata, when do I start? Do I get uniform like my sisters?'

Maama laughs so abruptly that it startles me. It is not a nice laugh. Taata scowls at her.

'You mean, girl, you think you are good enough to go to school with your sisters?'

'But Taata said…'

'Taata says you will go to school, yes.'

'Then…?'

'You think you are clever enough to go to school with them? You must attend school on the other side of town, where the stupid children go.' I can feel Taata stiffen against me.

'Leave it,' he warns. I rarely see Taata angry, but he sounds it now. He does not look at me though, his eyes are fixed on Maama. She heeds his warning and stops wagging her spiteful tongue.

'But I still get to go to school?' I look at Taata, and his eyes soften again.

'Yes, my child, you will go to the other school.'

I smile and hug him again. He smiles at me, but his eyes look sad. He wants me to go to the same school as the others, but I won't argue. School is school, and I'm grateful to have Taata on my side.

Chapter Two

At last, my first day arrives. I wake early and dress in the only clothes I own, a plain cotton outfit, faded from my long walks in the sun. The day before I had slipped it off and scrubbed it when Maama wasn't looking. It had meant wearing it wet for the rest of the afternoon, but I so wanted to look sharp for my first day. I skip down the hallway and sit at the table ready for breakfast. Breakfast, a luxury only given to the girls off to school. My stomach flutters and my mouth waters. The house is still quiet, my sisters dressing sleepily in silence. I allow myself a moment to enjoy the peace. I spy the empty jerry cans. Maama will be furious that I no longer do the task for her.

I hear footsteps in the hall. It is Maama.

'Maama, I go to school today.' I cannot contain my excitement.

'So, this makes you think you are better than me now?' Her eyes look sharp, fierce, but she does not shout.

'I do not understand, Maama?'

'Well, here you are dressed, sitting at *my* table, I assume you think you have earned the right to eat?'

'The big girls always have breakfast before school.'

'You have not earned the right to sit on my chairs or eat with my family. You must still work; you do not make this family proud just yet.'

'Work?'

'You think you no longer have to work?'

She can't expect me to still retrieve the water? There is no time before school.

'The water will wait, but you must sweep the floor, and wash the girls before you leave. And you get down from my table. You have not earned the right to sit there. You must sit on the floor. Like the dog that you are.'

Tears sting my eyes. I fight to stop them falling. I remind myself I will be going to school.

I start sweeping the floor before my sisters make it to the table. I am not given any breakfast. At least when I fetched the water, I couldn't smell the food. When I wash the plates, I wolf down the bits of crust the others have left. Once I have washed the girls, I ensure I am ready at the door. Maama passes the school bags to my sisters, each weighed down with books and pencils. There is no bag for me. I do not have books yet, so perhaps I don't need one. She hands out money for lunch to the others but not to me. She has not given me breakfast and without money, I cannot get lunch either.

'Ready my girls?' Taata appears from the bedroom he shares with Maama. He is dressed in his smart blue shirt over his navy trousers, ready to work, as he reaches me, he stops, 'Ah, little Lela, look at you, all ready for your big day.' He bends to my level, kissing my hand as though I am royalty.

'Yes, Taata.'

'Good girl. Come now, ladies, we must not be late.' I follow to get in the car, but I feel a hand on my shoulder. It is Maama. I feel her nails through my shirt. Taata turns to see where I have got to.

'Let her go, we must get to school.'

'You cannot possibly drop Lela at school.'

'Yes, I always drop the girls.'

'But you will be late if you drop Lela, her school is through the slums. You will never get the car through the crowds at this time.'

'So, you intend for her to walk?'

'She is used to it.' She pushes me away in the direction of school.

'I do not know the way.' I look at Taata for help, he opens his mouth to argue but Maama gives him a look and so he closes it again.

'You will find it, if you are as clever as you think you are. Head for Bwaise, and you will get there.'

I feel a stab of anger and for a moment I am tempted to rail at her, but I am worried she will stop me from going altogether, so I decide against it. I have not been to my school and I know I will be late by the time I find it. I have not been to Bwaise before either, but I have heard the stories. Thousands of people crammed into tiny tinned houses, just one room for a whole family. Children screaming, poverty, hunger, sewage and The Death.

I walk and I walk. It is much longer than my usual journey to the pump. I am far from the quieter suburban routes near home. The streets are even more crowded, there is shouting. Men yell at each other from their homes, no friendly waves or smiles, just bitter voices. A naked child sits in the street and calls for his mother, but there is no sign of her. Cars and minibuses honk their horns, but the traffic doesn't move. Eyes are looking at me. Does it show that I am not from these parts? My dress is clean while they are covered in mud and dirt. I keep my head down.

The sun is growing hot. As the streets are warmed a stench fills the air, which is so strong, I have to cover my nostrils. It smells like a latrine all around me. I hurry, aware that I am very late already, also hopeful that I can escape the smell. There is no sign of a school. My feet are blistered in my sandals and I am thirsty. Not only did I not get breakfast, but I have had no water either. I must ask someone. I look for a friendly face amongst the crowds. A young girl sweeps the street outside a shack, the building is crumbling around her, part of the roof missing, the only shelter coming from some corrugated iron propped up by the walls in one corner. Hordes of children hang around the entrance, their naked bellies overhanging their shorts.

'Excuse me? Where is the school? I am lost?'

'Girl, you is late for school, they shall beat you.'

'Please?'

'Go down there you will see it.'

My palms sweat as I head in the direction she has pointed out. The word 'beat' echoes inside my head. To be beaten on my first day at school! I run as I approach the entrance, shaving off every minute that I can. My sisters' school looks nothing like this. There are no gates here. The building is open, no glass in the windows and no door to the entrance. I see the children from where I stand on the street, some at desks but most leaning on walls, or sitting on the floor. The room looks much too small for so many pupils. The teacher sees me, but ignores me, until I step closer. He is very tall, his skin as black as night with not a hair on his shiny bald head. In his hand he holds a long wooden cane. I dare not think what he uses that for.

'Who is this?' he bellows.

'I am Lela.' My voice is just a whisper.

'You are late, we expected you at eight, I do not allow lateness in my class.'

'I am sorry, I did not know my way.' I try to explain.

'You will not talk unless I ask you a question. Bend down.'

I shake my head, but he forces me down and strikes my back with his cane. I feel my skin tear beneath the fabric of my dress, I cry out in pain. A little girl holds my gaze as I am whipped. I wonder if any of the children laugh like my sisters do, but they are frightened and dare not snigger. Once my thrashing is over, I am shown to an empty space on the floor. He shouts as I have no books. He says I should be reading by now. How can I read when no one has taught me?

I feel so ashamed, a feeling so far from the pride I thought I would experience on my first day at school, but I try to focus. I wish to learn. I try to make the 'vowel' sounds with my tongue. I focus on the shapes on the black board and try to remember the sounds that go with each. My head hurts from my walk with no water and my stomach rumbles.

At lunch we are excused to use a hole in the ground as a toilet, the only privacy coming from a wooden screen, then we are told to find ourselves some food. Most children have a few pennies and I watch them buy mandazi from a local man riding his bicycle down the street, the back of his basket bulging with the freshly baked donuts. They eat hungrily, and I am offered none. Before we are called back to the classroom an older girl approaches me. I do not look her in the eye. I worry she has come to beat me too or tease my ignorance. She throws a pencil in the dirt by my feet.

'I have a spare, use it,' she says.

'Thank you,' I look up at her and wonder if we may become friends, but she stalks off without a word. I avert my eyes, grateful for her kindness. I understand she does not wish to be associated with me.

The teacher gives me one book and I am told to guard it with my life for I shall not get another. I hold it tight, proud to at last have something of my own. I work hard to keep up with the other children, but he scoffs as he looks over my shoulder.

At last the day has come to an end, it has not been the first day I had imagined so many times and I am grateful I am dismissed. Once again, the streets are busy, and it takes me some time to orientate myself. By the time I know I'm on the right path it is growing dark. A man shouts at me:

'Pretty girl, come to my bed.' I do not understand. I have my own bed, why would I want to go to his? I keep my head down low and increase my pace, hoping he will not follow me. Instead, he calls to a tall woman, who tells him to shut his face. At last I am heading out of Bwaise and I begin to feel safer. There are fewer people to shout at me here, spaces between the houses, long shadows are cast where the sun has dipped below the horizon and the evening birds make their song in the tall trees. My nerves are settled by their call. In the distance I can see the lights from the area I know so well, I am not far from home, at last.

My feet, blistered and bloody from my ill-fitting shoes, limp as our house comes into view. I am ravenous and can't wait for dinner, but as I near I see the unmistakable, sturdy form of Maama, jerry cans in her hands, holding them out to me.

'Get a move on child, or you will miss dinner.'

'Tonight?'

'Always, what makes tonight any different?' She drops them in front of me and walks lazily into the safety of home.

Chapter Three

'Chapati,' a voice calls. A few children look up from their work, tentatively, Mr. Joram is tracing the shapes of letters onto the board. He checks his watch. 'Chapati,' the man's voice, closer this time, repeats.

In front of me one of the older boys scrawls something on a piece of paper and passes it to me. I look at the rows of loopy lettering but can't make head nor tail of it.

'She can't read, moron.' The girl across from me sneers in a sharp whisper, never removing her eyes from the back of Mr. Joram's head.

'What does it say?' I enquire. She rolls her eyes, snatching the note from me.

'He wants you to climb out the window and go and buy chapati for him.' She looks across to the boy, 'She doesn't have any money either, you idiot.'

'Good story honey, but in what part do you shut up?'

'Wipe your mouth, there's a little bit of cow poo around your lips'

'I really don't have any money.' I mouth at him.

'See, told you.'

'That better not be talking I hear back there,' Mr. Joram doesn't look back but finishes his sentence and rests his chalk gently on his desk. 'I am going out to buy my lunch, I expect you all to have copied down the text by the time I return.'

'You have your entire life to be a half-wit, why not take today off?' The boy gestures rudely as soon as Mr. Joram is out of sight. 'I *know* she doesn't have any money. I can give her some.'

'I can't go out there. Mr. Joram is buying chapati. He will see me. Why should I do it? What's in it for me?'

'Well I was going to give you enough money for you to get one for yourself, but, if you don't want to...' He flashes a crisp note at me.

'Why don't you just buy some at lunch?'

'Because the chapati man is long gone by the time he lets us go... I have to sit here for the next hour smelling his chapati all wrapped up and then go and buy boring mandazi from that old guy and it always tastes like the old boy has pissed on it.'

'He's not wrong.' The girl agrees.

'You squeeze out the window if you want it so bad.' I cross my arms. I'm not going to be pushed around just because I'm small.

'I can't fit out the window. Have you seen the size of this bottom?' He stands up and shakes it in my face and farts. Everyone erupts laughing.

'Urgh.' I hold my nose in disgust, 'You are sick.'

'Look,' He sits back down and stares at me, 'He will be back in a minute, are you going to do it or what? You're the smallest, only you can fit through. Crawl out now and hide, when he walks in, you go buy our chapati, then we will distract him until you come back.'

I look at him while I consider. I am always in trouble anyway, because I'm always late. Besides, I'm starving.

'Okay. Give me the cash.' I leap to my feet, 'But only if I can buy one for myself.'

'Yes!' He hands over his note.

'Wait. Get me one.' The girl throws me some extra change. The rest of the class look on, slightly bemused. Perhaps they want some, but I don't think sneaking in fifty chapatis will go down so well.

'Quick, go!' Out of the side window I see Mr. Joram paying his respects and turning to leave. I launch my whole body through the small hole. I am surprised at how easy it is. I shoot through like a bullet from a gun, falling on my face in the dirt. I hear the school kids giggle. Mr. Joram comes back into the class and hushes them all. The chapati man is leaving so I hurry, keeping low to the ground, and hide behind a poor excuse for a bush.

'Pssst!' I hiss. He looks puzzled and turns around. 'Down here.'

'What are you doing, child?' he calls, seeing my head pop out from the foliage.

'Shhh! Three chapatis please.'

'Why are you down there?'

'Please, hurry.'

He tuts and shakes his head, Poor crazy girl.' But he shovels three chapatis into their paper bags.

'Thank you!' I throw the money to him and crawl back towards the back wall of the school room.

I poke my head up. Mr. Joram's head is once again facing the board and he hasn't yet noticed my absence. I nod to show the mission has been a success, the boy gives me a thumbs up, and I prepare to climb back through.

'Oh Sir, snake! Mamba! Sir, above the board.' Mr. Joram drops his chalk and jumps backwards.

'Where boy, where?!' The class erupts into chaos, some laughing as Mr. Joram dances, brushing his hands over his body, others screaming and standing on their desks, searching the room for the mythical mamba. I launch myself back through the window. It's harder in this direction, as the ground is lower on the outside.

'There sir, there.' The boy yells again as Mr. Joram shows signs of turning, then offers a hand to pull me through. The chapatis are quickly distributed and hidden under our clothing and the classroom evacuated for fear of the imaginary snake.

An hour later, after standing under the hot sun while the classroom was thoroughly searched, we are allowed our lunch break. I eat with my partners in crime, cooled under the shade of a palm. The chapati tastes like heaven. We hold our chapatis up in a gesture of toasting. I feel a small wave of happiness. It feels like being accepted.

When we are dismissed for the day, I hurry home. With a chapati in my stomach and the possibility of friendship, I feel that things are looking up. Darkness is falling and it's getting harder to see. The shadows are playing tricks on my eyes. Ahead of me, I see the shape of a man. I approach cautiously. He is still. 'Is someone there?' I call out, but there is no reply, nor movement.

'Hello?'

The shadow begins to come into focus. It is indeed a man, a man tied to the branch of the tree by a rope. His arms and legs dangle, he hangs limp, a soft breeze is blowing from the direction of the lake and his body moves delicately, the rope squeaking as it rubs against the bark of the trunk.

'Sir?'

The breeze twists him towards me. The rope is tied into a noose around his neck. In the soft moonlight his eyes are bulging, A single, skinny line of blood emerges from his left nostril and smears of vomit drip from the corner of his mouth. A noise emerges from my throat, more of a groan than a scream, but I pull my hands up sharply to my mouth to prevent any further sound. Panic overwhelms me, and I no longer know which way home is. I want my Taata, why is he not here? I try to run but my body feels weak. My throat tightens, and I retch. I want to vomit but nothing comes. Somewhere behind me I hear a branch snap. I run, not caring which way, so long as I get as far away from Bwaise as quickly as I possibly can.

In my head I still see the look on the hanging man's face, I see him everywhere, he is on every house, on every branch. His bulging eyes look at me from every car that passes. Eventually I recognise the streets once more, the battered coffee shop where the old men play mweso. The regular faces are nowhere to be seen, safe in their homes, tucked up for the evening. Safe. At last I allow myself to stop, unable to catch my breath, my hands, shaking. This time, in the safety of my home 'village', I vomit, bright yellow sick into the street. A woman, hurrying home for the night, draws her own child closer to her breast as she passes me and shakes her head. I kneel in the gutter and cry. I cry for myself, for the man, for what I have seen, which can never be unseen.

I rise slowly and gather my book and pencil from the gutter, clutching them tightly to my chest. My home is in sight and I hurry through the darkness to make it back inside. As I lurch through the doors Taata is there to greet me, waiting anxiously for my return.

'Lela, my child, where have you been? Are you ok? How was school? Lela girl, you look sick,'

'Oh Taata.' the tears once more begin to fall, I can see Maama and the girls staring at me, not with concern but annoyance. I cannot help it, now I have started it is impossible to stop, I can barely breathe, the air catching in my throat.

'Now child, you are exhausted, come now, have some food.' There is no dinner ready yet, but he gives me fruit and some water. I eat slowly, struggling to get it down with the queasiness and the tears. I force myself to swallow and once I have eaten, I feel a little better. He smiles at me.

'Taata, he was dead, the man was dead.' My hands still shake, he looks at me in concern, I want him to hold me, to tell me that I never, ever have to return to Bwaise, but Maama is standing guard.

'What man? Lela tell me.'

'The man... in the tree.'

'You, Lela, are late.' Maama approaches, Taata takes my hand, holding it tight in his own, not looking at his wife. Today I have witnessed the worst thing in my entire life, and I cannot even fathom an excuse for not yet sweeping the yard. She walks to the edge of the kitchen and hovers over the empty jerry cans.

'We don't need your tales about dead men. Dead men don't climb trees.' Caroline sniggers. 'Go fetch the water.'

'Now?' I look at the darkness through the window, my body quivers.

'It is late, let the child rest.' Taata still holds me, he glares at Maama, his voice steady, but strong. 'Look at the state of her.'

'Well I presume you don't expect me to do it? She must still pay her way. Lela, water now or no dinner.' Taata shakes his head at her, but she ignores him. She nudges the nearest jerry can with her foot. I hesitate in disbelief, but I know she is serious. I cannot afford to miss another meal, and at least it is a walk I know well. I gather the jerry cans as she begins to peel matooke for dinner.

Chapter Four

'You have lost your spirit, girl.' Taata says, some days later. He lightly brushes my shoulder as he wanders into the kitchen for water. I have returned with the jerry cans and he has found me staring solemnly at empty saucepans. Since I started school, I eat less than ever. I am now settled into the school routine, yet my body remains sore and my belly hurts from emptiness. I feel exhausted.

'Still hungry?' Taata asks as I gaze longingly at the saucepans. Some days there is still food for me. Maama says if I hurry home from school then I can fetch the water quickly, then I might get a full belly. She doesn't care how far I walk every day. She makes me get the others ready for school before I leave, so I am always late, and I always get beaten. By the time I make it home again she claims I have dawdled, and I get beaten again. She made the girls' favourite meal tonight, I am sure to taunt me. The smells of meat and spices hang in the air and my belly growls. There are never any leftovers. I am rarely home before dusk anyhow, but last night it was pitch once again before I made it through the door, so Maama was raging. Taata refused to let me fetch the water and did it himself. Maama said it wasn't his place, that he had earned the money for the family, that he needed to rest and be looked after by his women. But he went anyway, and she beat me once he had left. After yesterday, I hadn't even cared.

The dead man continued to haunt me. In Uganda, death is a common part of everyday life. Our neighbour got sick and died last year. I remember her children screaming for their mother throughout the night, only growing silent from exhaustion as dawn broke. Death from sickness is unavoidable. It is the way things work and we have no say in it. But to take a life? Did someone hang him on that branch, or was it something he did to himself? I had been thinking about it as I raced home from school yesterday. I still hoped to be home early enough to eat dinner, I also hoped I could make it off the streets quickly. I was making good progress; the traffic was not yet at its peak and I could cut across the busier streets. Above me birds called playfully, and I followed their calls, spreading my arms to pretend I was one of them, high above the crowds, away from the trouble. I leapt over piles of rubbish littering the streets, gutters full of sewage, in and out of crowds of children playing, away from the men that called for me. I was a parrot, beautiful and free, others admired me, my looks, my joyful spirit. How I longed to be admired. I was so engrossed in my game I took a wrong turn down a street which was so quiet I was immediately on guard. The crowds were scary but being alone in Bwaise is scarier still. I felt as if I was being watched. I retraced my footsteps, then suddenly a man fell beside me. He was covered in blood, his clothes ripped, bare flesh wounds on show. His appearance shocked me, and I fell backwards against a wall. He struggled for breath as though he had been running.

'Help, help me,' he gasped, holding out his shaking arm towards me. His face fell in the dirt, trying to catch a breath but choking from the dust.

I wanted to help him, but my body remained glued to the wall. I had never seen so much blood. It stained the ground beneath him. I heard footsteps running up the alley. More men. They were upon me before I could hide.

'There he is.' They pointed at the body on the floor, then pulled him to his feet. A tall man, dressed in a skin-tight black t-shirt fought his way to the front of the throng as they propped him up, he no longer had the strength to stand on his own.

'You steal from me, and you will pay the price,' He shouted with a rage I have never seen. His face so close to the bleeding one, whose eyes were cast down to his own blood in the sand.

'Look at me, you thief.' He clenched his teeth, white against the black of his skin, like a dog before it tears through its prey. The bleeding man looked up at me. His eyes filled with tears.

'You, girl, come here.' the angry man called to me. I could not move. Someone grabbed my arm, dragging my feet along the ground, towards the blood. I was terrified, and suddenly had the urge to pee, convinced I would wet myself.

'You see this man? He is a thief, do you know what happens to thieves?' The other men began cheering as he spoke.

'Thieves need to pay for what they have done don't they?' I did not respond, 'Don't they?' He shouted at me this time and the grip around my arm tightened. I nodded quickly. 'This man shall pay for stealing from me, and you shall watch. You will learn to never be a thief.'

They dragged the thief back towards the main street. His screams pierced the air and stopped the traffic. The street fell still. It was a scream which can only come from a dying man. A crowd gathered, not stopping until they reached a clearing in the houses where a bunch of children were playing football. The children stopped as soon as the stench of danger hit, then they scattered. Two older boys stayed to watch, a decision they were sure to regret. I tried to slink away, hopeful that I had been forgotten, but the fingers clenched tightly as I struggled, and the nails dug into my skin.

The sound of a body thrown heavily to the ground echoed around the buildings and the crowd fell silent, anticipating the fall out. The man in the black T-shirt began to circle the thief, his screams now diminished, only occasionally sobbing.

'This swine has stolen from me and from many others. He will die today.'

The thief, barely able to speak, mustered the last of his energy to beg for his life.

'It is too late for apologies.'

'It was for my family, they are sick.'

'That is no excuse, thieves will be punished.'

His companions busied themselves, collecting dried out sticks, and newspapers, throwing them into a large pile. Others appeared with branches. I was desperate for him and for myself. I just wanted to get away.

Somebody threw petrol, and then a match and a fire began to roar within seconds. The crowd was riled up then, shouting and yelling. The thief curled into a ball, all his hope, lost. I closed my eyes. If I had to stay, I didn't want to watch. I closed them for as long as possible, the shouting intensified as orders were given to tie his hands and feet, then to swing his body into the flames. I smelled flesh burning. The last of his strength went into a final ear-piercing scream as he was burnt alive. I was grabbed by the back of the hair and my chin was forced upwards.

'Look girl, you must look.' I forced my eyes open, to see the thief's eyes were no more. His limbs were charred and he had no more fight left. His clothes burnt away and all that remained was a jet-black silhouette lying on a bed of flames. As his life left him the crowd became bored. One by one, they returned to their homes. In this district I expect many had seen these sights before. The grip on my arm was released and I found myself free to go. I can't say how long I stayed. I stood on this side of the cinders, alone except for the two boys, side by side, fixed to the spot, their eyes as wide as saucers.

On my way to bed, I recognise that my body is weak like that of yesterday's thief, he too had lost the fight, and as Taata could see, I was losing mine. As I head towards my room the world begins closing in on me and the last thing I see is Taata running towards me and catching me as I fall.

Chapter Five

As I open my eyes I am momentarily confused. I can hear shouting, but I know I am no longer in the kitchen. The light is dimmer, and I am staring up at the familiar cracks in the wall by my mattress. My eyes skim around the room. The other girls are peering down at me. Caroline kicks at the sheets. I wait for Josephine to start shouting at me, telling me the fighting is all my fault, but she looks away and stares at the floor instead. I sit up, still a little woozy, my head spins slightly, but I steady myself. Next to my mattress is a plate of posho and a glass of water, I grab hungrily at the posho and turn my back, again, on the others, shoving as much into my mouth in one go as is humanly possible. I am aware that I resemble the starving children I have seen on the way home from school, fighting over scraps, then almost choking on them when they put too much in their mouths. I do not want the others to see me like that, but I am so hungry I can't help it. As my chewing eventually slows, I can hear Maama and Taata clearly. I am surprised it is Taata doing most of the talking. He sounds enraged and I am scared. Taata is my favourite person in the world, I cannot bear to think that I have upset him.

'How dare you, you have not fed her for how long?'

'She eats when she has finished her work.'

'But does she? There was no food for her tonight.'

'It is not my fault if she is too late for food.'

'Why did you not save her any? She is just a *child*.'

'Her *mother* does not pay for the food in this house, I did not *ask* her whore of a mother to sleep around and have that brat. I did not *ask* for her to be brought here. Why should I pay for her food, and soap, and clothes? I am *not her mother*.'

There is silence. Taata doesn't immediately respond. Suddenly things make sense. All the years of chores, different schools, no food. I am unloved, I am unwanted. She is not my Maama, she does not want me. My real mother doesn't want me either. My throat has tightened, and I try my hardest not to cry but the tears, and the posho, are choking me, my eyes burn.

'Lela,' Faith speaks, I turn my head to scowl at her. I do not want their pity, they are not my sisters, they don't want me either. She sees my look and stares down at her feet, the others are doing the same. They look ashamed, but I do not understand why they should feel this way. They are wanted, they are *loved*, it is I who doesn't belong here. If they are not my family, if *she* is not my mother then who is? Taata is speaking again, quieter now and I must control my sobs, so I can hear.

'Keep your voice down,' he warns

'Or what?'

'She does not deserve to find out this way, she's a good kid.'

'She is just like her mother, she will go nowhere, she will sleep around and have more brats just like herself. She may as well know now.'

'Why are you doing this? What has she done to you?'

'How can you ask that? All these years I have had to look after her. For what? For nothing! I get no thanks, nothing in return.'

'Stop talking like this, woman,'

'Why should I stop? She is a *nothing.*'

'She is a *child.*'

'She is a *nobody.*'

Deep sobs continue to form at the back of my throat, making it ache, but I cannot stop them. My mother doesn't want me, my schoolteacher beats me, this woman who I have grown up with loathes me. But I know I'm somebody.

'Stop it,' he shouts over my crying.

'I won't. If you want her so much, have her, but it is HER or ME.'

'What do you mean?'

'If you want *her* to stay, I am leaving.'

'She has nowhere to go, we are her family.'

'*I* am NOT her family. If she stays, I go.'

'She is staying.'

'You choose her over me? Your wife?'

'She stays.'

'That *bastard* stays? Then goodbye.' I stop crying and I am frozen in terror. I can hear Maama crashing around her room, gathering her belongings. The other girls are watching the door too. They cannot believe what they are hearing. They do not want their mother to leave, but after long minutes of angry stomping around, she walks out. I have no idea where she will go at this hour. We wait breathlessly in silence, but she doesn't reappear. She has really gone. Taata knocks lightly on the door and looks at the four of us.

'I'm sorry you had to hear that, girls.' He looks at me. 'Lela, please can you come with me.'

I rise slowly from my mattress. My legs feel weak, but he takes my hand, closing the bedroom door behind us. He leads me towards the kitchen and seats me on a chair. If Maama caught me on a chair I would be in so much trouble. I am eyeing up the door, expecting her to enter at any moment.

'Lela, Lela, look at me.' Taata gently moves my chin to face him. I look at his features. There are no signs of anger anymore, he looks tired and sad.

'Lela, my child, you were to learn one day that we are not your parents, but I didn't want it to happen this way. I am sorry you do not get to eat dinner regularly and Maama has not been treating you with kindness. I care very much for you. I may not be your real Father, but to me you will always be a daughter, no matter what Maama says. She is an angry woman, but it is not your fault.'

I am grateful for his kind words, but my heart feels hollow.

'Lela, I will take care of you.' This evening has exhausted me. He sees this too and picks me up as though I am a baby once more. He carries me back to our room and walks across to my mattress, telling me to wait on it while he fetches the bed from the spare room. After some effort a small single bed fits neatly alongside those belonging to the girls I once classed as sisters. I feel I belong on my mattress, but I get into the bed.

'This is your bed now.' He gently lays me down; the bed feels soft and warm. He pulls the sheets to my neck and tucks them around my body. They feel smooth on my skin. Taata tells the other girls to sleep. No one argues, no one tells him that I do not belong in that bed. I close my eyes and sleep soundly.

It's a lot later than dawn when I wake. The beds beside me are empty and light streams through the small window above the doors which lead to the outside. The air in the room is stuffy and warm, like it usually is around noon. Our room is rarely comfortable. Built as a garage, it is either too hot during the day or too cold at night. When I wake at dawn there are a few moments when I feel warm, today it must be late as I am sweating. I kick the sheets off my legs and enjoy a moment of peace. The house is silent. I can hear children playing in the compound, there is laughter echoing around the buildings. Although deep down there is an emptiness which feels new, I also feel strangely at peace. I now understand why Maama was always so angry at me. The silence tells me she can't have returned.

I move slowly from my bed. I do not want to leave immediately, despite the heat. I feel sure that I will return to my mattress again very soon, so want to take full advantage of my time in a proper bed. There are footsteps heading down the hall and I flinch, but no one comes my way. I am not used to being left to my own devices, fully expectant that someone will bark orders at me at any moment. I want to stay forever in this bed, but I feel guilty suddenly that I am not doing my work, so I rise and dress quickly, then head down the hall to the kitchen. Taata is busying himself and doesn't see me immediately. I can hear him humming quietly. He looks strangely calm as he chops fruit at the table. His back is towards me and I notice how grey his hair has become. The sudden awareness of his age startles me. He looks up suddenly as he catches the same smell that I do, something is burning. His bare feet dash across the concrete floor as though they themselves are on fire and he hurriedly remove a pan from the stove, muttering something under his breath. I can't help but giggle, it is very unusual to see Taata cook and it is evident that he is not very good at it.

'Ahh Lela, you have woken.' He looks happy to see me. He beckons me to sit at the table and then calls the other girls in from outside. I am surprised that they are not at school, but having said that, neither am I. The three come running in, smiles light up their faces, their hair plastered to their foreheads with sweat. Josephine, the eldest one, is laughing as she comes through the door, but she abruptly stops when she sees me seated.

'Maama says you must *not* sit at the table,' she shouts. I jump from my chair but Taata stops me.

'Lela, sit. Josephine, Maama is not here. We play by my rules now. Lela will be eating with us from now on, understand?'

I stick my tongue out at her while Taata's attention is focused elsewhere. Born stubborn like her mother, she deserves more than that.

She glares at me but remains silent. Taata has put together a fine spread of food. It is wonderful to have a meal to eat, I do not even mind the burnt bits. The others push their food around their plates, Josephine complains that it is not as good as usual, but then says nothing more. Once they are finally excused, I polish off their leftovers.

'Well, glad to see someone likes my cooking.' Taata laughs. I have my mouth full and cannot reply but nod enthusiastically. He could have been the worst cook in the whole world, but I wouldn't have cared. He is feeding me. I am happier in this one moment than I can remember ever feeling before. As I finish my final mouthful, I see the jerry cans standing empty by the door. He has not lectured me to get a move on, but I do not want Taata angry, so I rise quickly from my seat and head over to them.

'No Lela, that is not your job today.'

'But someone must fetch the water. I must show my worth.'

'Lela, come here.' He grabs both my hands in his and pulls me to him. He lowers himself to my height and speaks softly. 'Lela, as I said last night, you are as much of a daughter to me as Josephine, Caroline and Faith. You have had no time to be a child. I cannot remember the last time I saw you laugh. You are always so tied up with housework, it is time to be a little girl. I have employed a boy in the village to collect the water. He will come every day. He is happy to be earning money for his family. I am happy as we will get our water, and you shall be happy as you will have time to play.'

I have never been allowed to play.

Just as Taata said, a boy arrives at the door, he says hello to me and then he walks off with the jerry cans. I step out of the house behind him and into the sunshine. For a moment I just stand and breathe, my eyes adjusting to the light, watching him head down the dusty road in the direction of the pump, the walk I myself have done hundreds of times before. My sisters have returned to their game, they are throwing a small ball to each other. Some older children I don't recognise call them by name and taunt them with the ball when it comes their way. Josephine manages to wrestle the ball back and throw it to Faith, but she misses it and the ball instead falls near my feet.

'Lela, Lela, throw it,' Faith laughs as she moves out of the way of one of the older children. I slowly bend and pick it up, feeling the firmness of it in my hand. I squeeze it gently. 'Come on Lela!' The girls call.

I smile and throw it to Faith. I do not have much practice at throwing, it ends up in a space between Caroline and an older girl. They both hastily go for it and trip each other up instead of collecting the ball. I laugh as the older girl finally gets hold of it.

'Hey, good throw,' she jokes.

I look at the other girls, certain one of them will tell me I am not welcome, and although Josephine glances at me, none of them say anything.

The exhilaration of play excites me. I find I am suddenly laughing, and sweating, and not caring when I fall. It is not the same sort of sweat provoked by the weight of the jerry cans. Although it is becoming harder to breathe, I barely notice as I run in and out of the girls in the hope of catching the ball once more.

Taata comes outside to sweep the compound but stops and watches us instead. He smiles a wide, broad smile, interrupted only by small bouts of laughter as one of us falls, or is caught. We play for what seems like hours, as suddenly the sun is lower in the sky and Taata calls us in to wash before we have our supper.

I stand alongside him, ready to wash the girls as I always do, but he moves me next to Faith, then gently removes my clothes and bathes me with warm water. The water makes me feel relaxed, comfortable. I am dressed in dry, clean clothes, clothes that are too immaculate to be my own, and once again I get to sit at the table.

Dinner is even more delicious than lunch, but my stomach is not used to so much food, defeated well before I can contemplate eating the other's leftovers. Taata chuckles.

'At last! I have filled your belly.' I grin, too full to move. The other girls laugh too, but, for once, not *at* me.

I have a strange sensation inside me this evening. A feeling of being loved and wanted. It is peculiar to suddenly feel accepted after years of nothing but neglect. Even more so that this feeling comes just so quickly after finding out this family are not mine, that the lady I had called Maama for the past six years wants nothing to do with me. After all that, now I sit on the living room chairs, watching television, with Taata's arm over my shoulders, and I feel like I belong.

Chapter Six

Two weeks since Maama left and I am happier and, I believe, healthier than I have ever been. Taata discovered that I had not been receiving any lunch money (to his horror) so now I get lunch every day, alongside breakfast and dinner too. Everyone remarks on the difference in me. My energy has returned. This week at school I even received a cup from Mr. Joram. I had never had any awards or compliments from him before, but he said he was so pleased that I now made it into class on time he wanted to praise me for it. I brought the cup home to show Taata, as I felt he had earned it just as much as me.

Caroline and Faith seem to like me now, they tell me stories about the girls at school, and always let me play ball with them. Josephine is still hostile, being the eldest, many of her mother's words well absorbed. Life is good, despite her cutting remarks. I try to erase the days before this time. No one has heard from Maama since she left, and I hope every day that she has gone for good. Taata says the sparkle has returned to my eyes.

It is the weekend and I am helping Taata cook. He burns most of the food. Not that I am complaining. Food is food, but the other girls are getting skinny! They say I need to show Taata how it is done. I have put on Maama's apron and am embracing the role of bossy Matriarch. 'No, you can't sit there! No, you don't do it like that! Silly girl don't sit in the chair.' I stuff my dress with tin cups to emphasise Maama's huge breasts and waggle my backside.

Taata guffaws, 'A scary resemblance!' He laughs hysterically when I hear a knock at the door.

'Can you get that please; my hands are covered in chicken.' His hands are stuffing the chicken's rear end. I giggle as I walk down the hall, removing the tin cups, I wonder if it is one of my new friends. I get called on most days after school.

The door swings back and hits me in the face. I draw my hand up to my nose in shock as a large body pushes past me.

'Get out of the way, *bastard*.' It is Maama.

Maama tears through the house like a cyclone. 'What the hell is cooking? Will you look at me!' The house is silent, aside from her barrage of criticism and the chairs scraping at the kitchen floor. The older girls have gathered, wide-eyed. Josephine looks eager to run to her, but Caroline holds her sister back. At last Taata speaks.

'Where have you been?'

'Where have I been? I am your wife, this is my home, or have you forgotten that?'

'I have not forgotten, I have not forgotten to look after our home, to look after *our* children. You stormed out with no contact. No message to let me, your husband, know that you are safe.'

'My business stopped being yours the day you chose that bastard over me. Why does she suddenly have the right to open the door? Wearing *my* apron! Why is she not getting water? Or washing the girls? Have you forgotten her place in the family as you seem so dead set in reminding me of mine?'

I want to vomit, or scream, or cry, or run. I can't contemplate going back to my old life. I have spent the last weeks in a state of bliss, believing that life could be good, that I could be happy. Now, I know it will be worse than it ever was before. She will not forgive Taata for choosing me over her. I can't go back to being treated like a despised servant. I am frozen in terror. I cannot bring my legs to move, my arms glued to the sides of my dress. I cannot summon a noise to rise from my throat. Caroline and Faith stare at me in pity and regret. I need them to know I am aware our time as friends is over. I have enjoyed feeling loved, wanted, appreciated as a person. I do not hold any of this against them.

Josephine seizes her moment and escapes Caroline and runs to her mother.

'Maama.' She calls and flings her arms around her mother. If only I could do the same with mine.

'My child. At least someone is happy to see me.'

'Maama, I have missed you so much, it's not the same without you. Lela has been terrible; she has disobeyed you so many times. Taata even stopped her getting the water, he has *paid* some horrible boy to come. Lela sits on the chairs Maama, every day.'

'*My* chairs?' My feet stick to the floor as I picture the look of disgust on her face.

'Yes Maama, your chairs, *and* she sleeps in the bed, Taata moved the spare bed to our room, the one you have reserved for guests. She has not even touched her mattress.'

'Taata, do you not see how upset Josephine is by this? Your own daughter.'

'Upset by what? Kindness? If you do not teach this child kindness soon no one ever will, and she will turn out just like you.' Taata heads out of the kitchen and down the hallway towards me.

He whispers into my ear. 'Stay strong, Lela.'

Then he walks out of the house. Panic gnaws at the pit of my stomach. I am entirely at her mercy.

I hear Maama talking to Josephine. 'I am sorry my girl that you've had to watch your Father slowly losing his mind. It cannot have been a happy home for you since I left.'

'No Maama,' Josephine is lapping up her mother's attention. She attempts a sob to add to the illusion of her misery.

'Well my dear, I think that brat needs to be put in her place, don't you?'

She comes for me. I see her now. Her eyes are narrowed, one hand clasped tightly around Josephine's. I can't help it, but I wet myself. I do not even notice it is coming until I feel the warmth trickle down my left leg, forming a stinking pool around my toes. I am deeply ashamed and look away.

'My God, you dirty child. He says you owe me nothing but look at the mess I am left to deal with, six-year-old children that still piss their pants. You are old enough to clean this up yourself. You filthy girl.' She strikes me with the flat of her palm, so hard that I fall on to the floor, and I'm soaked by my own puddle. She lets go of Josephine and pulls me straight back onto my feet, despite my sodden clothes. She shakes me until I cannot see straight. The colours of the hallway, the red and pink of Josephine's dress, the black of Maama's skin all merge into one.

45

'I will teach you. You shall never disobey me again. I am not your mother. I am *better* than your mother and I will always be better than your mother. Now the truth is out, I am no longer Maama to you. I am Iris. You call me Iris and if I ever hear you call me Maama again I shall beat you. I shall beat you so hard you will not sit down for a week. Do you hear me girl, you must hear me? You are a bastard. You shall be a bastard always.'

I feel nauseated and dizzy, but the shaking doesn't stop, she's been saving her pent-up rage especially for me. Finally, I fall like a dead weight back into my own puddle. Maama, no, Iris, has stopped. Caroline and Faith are crying and pulling at her arms. Even Josephine looks disturbed.

She has grown tired of tormenting me. I lie on the wet floor, afraid to move in case she attacks me again.

That woman, that woman who is not my Maama, Iris, returns to the kitchen but a few moments later six jerry cans are hurled at me.

'When you have finished wallowing in piss like an animal, clean it up and then fetch the water. Remember your place.'

I know, for now, the scene is over. I must return to the only other life I knew.

Chapter Seven

I have not yet fully paid for Iris having to depart her home and family for two weeks. I am back on my mattress and have barely slept. The worry has caused my stomach to tie itself in a knot and I have been up and down to the latrine every hour since midnight. Sometime around three I heard Taata enter through the kitchen door and creep down the hallway. I feel better that he's home.

The sun has begun to rise, and I am starting to feel warmth again in the room as the light filters through the tiny windows. Down the hallway there is movement and I know it is not the light-footed steps of Taata, but the loud stomping mass of the woman I used to call Maama. She crashes around her bedroom, the kitchen and then I hear her sigh as she heads towards our room. I sit up, back straight as a poker.

The door bursts open. Her heavy breasts heave with exertion. I pull my meagre sheet closer to my chin in fright, but she ignores me. Instead, she moves hastily towards the metal bedstead which was, so briefly, my bed. She tears off the thin coverlet and throws it to the floor. Followed by the pillow, the sheet, even the mattress gets torn from its place and flung to one side. I cower in the corner as debris flies around the room. As soon as the bed is stripped, she pulls it away from the wall. I am shocked by the sheer strength of this woman. In one swift movement it is a whole meter from the wall. Caroline, closest to the spare bed, has leapt onto Faith's and is clinging to her younger sister with fright. Josephine too is fully awake, bolt upright, in the furthest bed from her Maama. Her eyes are fixated on the drama unravelling. Iris has not spoken a word but moves methodically to pull the bed as far away from the wall as it will go. Once it is in line with the door, she changes direction, heaving the bed through the door frame and out of sight. We take a moment to look at one another. What is she planning? No one dares to move or speak. The metal screeches against concrete, then suddenly there is silence. Where is Taata? He cannot have slept through the noise? Then we hear her footsteps again. Caroline and Faith hold each other tighter, unsure of what is coming. Still Iris does not speak, simply moves onto Caroline's bed. She does the same thing, strips it and throws the bedding towards me. I am imprisoned by a wall of mattresses and blankets. Then the second bed frame is hauled through the doorway. Iris's strength does not falter.

As she returns to our room for a third time, Faith and Caroline jump onto Josephine's bed. I am trapped in my corner. The pile of mattresses like Kilimanjaro, I imagine the piles of sheets are the snowcapped peaks. I wonder what snow feels like to touch, the cold on my toes, the purity. Up there the air is clear, only the calls of the birds can be heard.

By the time Iris returns for the fourth bed she is drenched in sweat. She smells hot and salty. Behind my fortress I am struggling to breathe. She is tiring now, reaching the end of her mission. This bed appears heavier than the rest. Her movements have slowed and every now and then she props her weight against it to catch a breath. When she is finally exhausted, she pulls her weary feet again along the concrete floor, but she does not enter our room, simply calls as she passes.

'Josephine, Caroline, Faith, make up the beds in the spare room. This is to be your room now. Leave the bastard alone in her garage. Silently the girls obey, slowly tearing down my mountain to uncover my hiding place. I say nothing in return, my fist still clutching my threadbare sheet as the room is slowly emptied. Finally, it is only my mattress that is left. As Caroline returns to collect the final pillows, I can see she wants to speak. To mark the end of the time we have shared together. Her head is hung with shame, her shoulders hunched, tight.

I dress in the outfit Taata bought me for school. Although it is Sunday, it is the only other item of clothing I own, and my dress still reeks of urine. There is no sign of Iris now, I suspect she has returned to her bed to sleep off her exertion. I do not want to be in this house any longer and am grateful, for once, for the excuse to fetch water. Already my muscles have forgotten some of their duty. My legs buckle twice under the weight of the cans, and I need to rest several times on my walk. I do not hurry today. I am in no rush to get back home. I suspect there will be no food for me.

As I stop for my final rest before the house comes into sight, I take my time to watch the people around me. Many people are returning with water for their homes, most are children, like me, but many are women too. A lady walks alongside a little girl, who can be no more than three, yet already knows how to perfectly balance a jerry can of water on her head without spilling a drop. Her left hand gesticulates as she talks animatedly to the woman, who laughs loudly at the story she is being told. The little girl's eyes sparkle as she describes something. The woman looks pretty when she laughs. Her face comes to life. I wonder if this woman looks anything like my own mother. Did she know me once? I have no memory of her but, perhaps, I was too young to know. Maybe we talked like this together, her laughing at my stories. I would tell her of the hippos that wallow in the water holes, how they run, and she would laugh at my impressions. She would tell me gently that it is sleep time, so no more stories for tonight, and I would fall asleep in her arms as she caressed my hair. I think my own mother must be dead, for she cannot have left me to live with a mad woman if she were alive.

Iris is waiting for me as I return. Her body takes up most of the doorway and so I see it as soon as the house comes into view. She does not yell at me immediately, simply tells me to hurry as we have tasks to perform. I set my jerry cans down in the kitchen and stand in front of her awaiting my instructions. She is finishing the lunch preparations. Five plates sit side by side on the table. Three small ones and two larger ones. Before she calls for the family to eat, she pulls a small bundle from her pocket. I have seen her carry this bundle before and watch as she unwraps the contents. Inside is a small sachet. She takes a pinch from it and sprinkles it on Taata's plate. She sees me watching.

'For Taata, to help him sleep,' and she whisks it back into her pocket before anyone else sees. The family gather to eat their lunch. Taata nods at me when he sees me, but he does not speak, nor smile. His eyes are sunken, deep shadows below them, sweat beads gather on his forehead, he does not look well. Iris sets her plate to one side.

'Lela and I have work to do before we eat,' she announces. Taata hesitates before taking a bite of his meal, but it is clear to see he does not have any fight in him today.

I am steered out of the kitchen and ordered to walk along the path that leads behind our home. We are heading towards the grasslands. From under her skirt mother pulls two heavy duty sacks, the sort that I see filled with rice at the store.

'Fill these with grass, child.' It is a peculiar order, but I can't argue, so I pull at the grasses until the sacks begin to fill. Iris has sat a few meters away and is sunning herself, smoking on a pipe she has pulled from her bust, her face turned towards the sky. She laughs every now and then, as though my task is highly amusing.

'Make sure you fill them nice and full, or they won't be comfortable.'

'Why must they be comfortable?'

'Don't you know? These are to be your bed.'

'My bed?' The sacks feel course, their edges sharp.

'What's wrong? Have we spoilt you on your mattress? Yes, your bed child, do not answer back.'

I do as I am told and continue stuffing them with grass, more carefully now, choosing longer pieces from the verge and avoiding the dry patches. If I am to sleep on them, I do not want twigs sticking up and poking me in the night.

'We are to have a guest,' Iris continues. We often have visitors this is not news. 'He will stay a while, on your mattress, in your room. He can't be sharing with the other girls, now can he? Their room is too crowded, it must be even. He is a distant cousin. He's a little shit too, you should have a lot in common.'

She forces her legs to stand once more as I finish stuffing grass as quickly as I can, then we make our way back up the road to home. A visitor. She calls him a 'shit' like I have heard her call me, maybe, if we have so much in common, he may be a friend? I can only hope.

As the family arrange themselves around the table for supper, I am on the cold kitchen floor. At least I'm being allowed to eat. Taata emerges once more. He looks relieved when he sees me. He too does not question me sitting on the floor. I am shocked when I see the state of him. Sweat now flows freely down his face and I see his hand is shaking as he tries to pick up his food. The other girls have noticed, and they are staring. Maama put that powder on his food again. I hope it works this evening. He looks as though he needs his rest.

Before we have a chance to finish our dinner there is a knocking at the door. Iris rises before any of the children run to get it.

'That shall be our guest.' She announces. I gulp down the remainder of my plate before she barks any orders at me. My eyes remain fixated on the doorway, eager to see the boy that will be coming to stay.

'This is Mussa,' she says. I swallow my last mouthful, at last a potential friend, who I can confide in, a boy who shall share my room, and maybe be a shoulder to cry on? But as he emerges from behind her, I see the 'boy' is more a man. Long, lean legs, tall and somewhat gangly with acne all over his face. 'He is my brother-in-law's cousin, and he will stay here while he finds work in the area.' Taata, I notice, stops playing with the food he has yet been unable to stomach. He glances up at this skinny man with an absent look in his eye. He was clearly not expecting a guest.

'Lela, get up, you will show Mussa to his room.' she snaps at me. I jump to my feet quickly.

'Mussa, Lela will show you where you are to sleep then you can join us for some food.' He follows me down the hall to the bedroom I used to share with my sisters. I have set up my bed of sacks where my mattress used to lie, so that I can at least trace the familiar lines on the wall. I set my old mattress up for him of the far side of the room and I am pleased now that it is as far away from me as it could be. I am uneasy having to share with this stranger. I point the mattress out to him and inform him that is to be where he sleeps. He nods and doesn't seem concerned that he is on a mattress in a garage and not a proper bed. Iris can't think that highly of him, although obviously more so than me.

'Who sleeps there?' He tilts his chin upwards in the direction of the pile of sacks.

'That is where I will sleep.' I reply.

'Good.' His mouth widens into an unnerving grin. I see dirty, yellow teeth that sit crookedly in his square jaw. I do not like his smile and I wish I was back with the girls. At least he does not seem to mind sharing a room with me. I am not sure I could handle any more hostility.

Once I have returned from my tasks in the yard, he is already asleep. I am pleased as it means I can slip into my night clothes without being looked upon by a stranger.

I have returned to my old routine of having to get the girls ready for school before I can leave for my long walk. It means I am up early with the roosters. As Mussa is still sleeping, I try to make as little noise as possible. It is not difficult as the room has no furniture now, but the door creaks as I sneak out. Mussa stirs and glares at me.

'Will you be quiet, you *mbwagwe*, I'm sleeping.' he snarls at me. I am used to cruel words, but when they come from a stranger it makes them seem more hurtful, as though I truly deserve them. I rush down the hallway to escape his vicious tongue, keen to get to school, although I know I can only expect a beating for being late. Taata has, at least, made it to breakfast and is eating. He looks dazed, but healthier than yesterday.

I rush to school. Mr. Joram tells me how disappointed he is before he beats me. Weeks of being prompt, looking smart and now I turn up hot, bothered and late. At lunch I sit alone once more, watching the other children eat. I can see them watching me too. I don't mean to stare but my stomach has become used to food and without it hurts and growls uncomfortably.

'You don't eat today?' A girl named Farida approaches me. She has not spoken to me before, but she seems kind. I have watched her in class. She always tries to be a good student and to do well.

'I am not hungry,' I lie. I do not wish to be pitied. This is a poor neighbourhood but if you have the money to go to the school then you can scrape together some money for mandazi at lunch.

'You can share some of mine?' She asks, seeing straight through my lie.

I shake my head, I am too proud to take it in front of the other children, but I smile, and Farida sits next to me.

'You were late again today.'

'It is difficult, I do not have transport again so must walk, the last weeks were a holiday for me.'

'I walk too, but I don't live far away.' She smiles at me.

At least I seem to be making one friend. The thought buoys me up as I rush home with the jerry cans, eager to scout the pans for food. There is a plate on the side for Taata, who has not returned home yet, and I know better than to touch his food. He needs it to regain his strength. The pans are otherwise empty, and I can't help but feel dreadfully low at the thought of a night without anything in my stomach. Behind me I sense movement, it is Mussa.

'You come home late, you know, for a kid.'

'I have to fetch the water after school.'

'Here, I saved this for you.' He pulls some pineapple from his pocket. I smile gratefully.

'Thank you.' I am surprised by his kindness after the way he spoke to me this morning. He does not mention it though. Maybe he was sleep-talking. He seems kind now. I eat quickly before Iris sees it. Weighing up Mussa's actions, I think he is on my side after all.

Chapter Eight

I am asleep before Mussa has come to bed. I am in a deep sleep that takes me through until dawn. The sun is just beginning to rise when I am suddenly jolted from my sleep by a shock of cold water. My thin nightdress is cold and damp. I see the tall body of Mussa standing over me. He has poured a glass of water over my bed and is laughing.

'What are you doing?' I shout. He continues to laugh.

'You pee yourself like a baby.' He sneers at me.

'I do not, why do you throw water at me?'

'I did not, look at you, it's all over your bed, your Maama must see.'

'She is not my Maama and she should not.'

He has grabbed my arm and is already shouting, 'Iris, Iris, come, come!'

The house is silent. Iris will still be asleep at this time. Being woken will enrage her more than anything, I learnt that lesson once many years ago when I was sick in the night and I know not to make that mistake again.

'Please, shh, don't wake her.' I try to quieten him. Why is he doing this? I am so confused. Is it some sort of revenge for waking him yesterday? He must have forced himself to get up early just to do it.

'Why, why are you doing this?'

'Pipe down you dirty girl, you need to be taught a lesson. Iris!' He continues to shout down the hall until I hear the familiar pounding of Iris storming.

'Why you make all this noise Mussa? The house is sleeping, it is too early, why do you hold Lela like that? What has she done to you?'

'She woke me by pissing in her bed! I woke up to see her standing there, pissing like an animal.'

She examines my night shirt and the drenched sack of grass.

'Why you do this girl? After I provide you with a bed, food, this is how you repay me by pissing in my house like an animal? You dog, you will learn from this.'

Mussa is trying not to smile, though I see his crooked teeth.

'What will you do, Iris?'

'I shall beat her like a dog. Mussa, I am sorry you have had to witness this; you may go back to bed now.'

She drags me outside, her nails digging into me as they have so many times before. Mussa lazily follows us.

'Bend down, girl.' She orders me across her lap. I do so, I know that fighting only makes her hit harder. She gets the long cane she keeps near the latrine, reserved entirely for me. How lucky I am. I clench my buttocks and prepare for the strike. It comes hard and fast. No matter how much I expect it the first always makes me inhale sharply. I tighten my face to try and avoid any expression. I can't see Mussa, but I hear him say: 'Wait Iris, wait, she will not learn if you beat her like this.'

She looks up at him, annoyed. I don't think Iris has ever expected to take tips on beating a small child from anyone.

He rips my nightdress to expose my naked flesh to the world. My back and bottom are now on show.

'Yeah, there you go,' he mutters as his hand runs from the top of my shoulder blades all the way down. He stops when he reaches my buttocks and slaps one of them sharply, 'Yeah, just there should do it.'

Iris whips the cane down onto my skin. My skin tears and I cry out in pain.

'Yeah, that's how you do it, Iris!'

'Oh yes, Mussa, perfect.' She guffaws, 'perfect.'

Blood trickles down my legs. I stop squealing with each strike and they grow bored. Iris pushes me from her lap, and I land like a sack of rice in the dirt. She and Mussa stroll inside.

I gather up my tattered nightdress and rush to the latrine. No matter how hard I try and tie it, I cannot cover up my back, nor the damage they have done to me.

'Girl, girl, you in there?' I hear a voice, one I'm not familiar with. It sounds calm and gentle, kind. The sort of voice I am learning not to trust. I decide I shall not answer.

'Girl, I know you are in there, I saw you go in there with my own eyes. I saw what they did, will you talk to me?'

Still I do not reply.

'I live in the house behind you, I know how she treats you girl, I see what she does.' A tear rolls down my nose and I wipe it away quickly.

'Look, you do not have to speak to me, but as she has beaten you there will be no breakfast.'

I don't think I will survive the walk to school with nothing in my stomach.

'I have left some food here, just behind the latrine. I have pushed it through the gap in the fence. Eat quickly before she calls for you again.'

I wait a few minutes. I hear footsteps slowly move further into the distance, then a door swinging closed. I move as fast as my damaged skin will allow. As promised, behind the latrine is a plate piled with matooke and beans. I make sure Iris and Mussa are nowhere near, then force each mouthful in. I peek through a hole in the fence, but I don't see my neighbour.

Chapter Nine

I do not understand the ways of grown-ups.

After the beating, Mussa did not speak to me for the rest of the day. However, the following day he yet again saved me food and asked how my buttocks were feeling. I did not know what to say. I couldn't even sit down at school the morning it happened. My teacher asked me why I was so fidgety. I had to lie. Eventually he whipped my knuckles and sent me home. I barely flinched; I think I was becoming used to pain.

I had to tiptoe into the house. I was not due home for hours. I feared being seen by Iris or Mussa. The house was quiet. At first, I thought everyone was out, but the door was unlocked. Mussa at least was gone. His shoes were not lined up by the front door, and he was not in his usual place, stretched out in front of the television. I suspect he was out job hunting. The girls were at school and Taata at work, but I heard voices as I crept into the kitchen.

I edged further down the hallway to see where the sound was coming from. Without a doubt it was Iris's voice, but it sounded different. She was in her bedroom giggling, almost like a little girl. Strange, as she so rarely laughed. Not even Taata made her laugh these days. I wondered, at first, if she was giggling to herself but then I heard a male voice alongside hers. The man was speaking in a low, soft tone, so I couldn't hear what he was saying. The voice was deeper than Mussa's, and Taata's.

I tiptoed to the back entrance which, to my relief, was propped open. I slipped through it and hid in the small gap between the latrine and the back fence. I rested my body on my knees, as I still could not sit on my bottom.

'So, you are back then?' An elderly lady peered over the fence watching me. I recognised her voice. It was she who had left me the food that morning. I jumped to my feet and stared at her. She was old, much older than Iris, and very short. She stood on tiptoes to see over the fence, which I could almost see over already. Her grey hair was cut very short, almost to her scalp, and her face covered in soft lines, particularly around her eyes, so she looked like she was smiling, even when she wasn't. I was still too scared to speak.

'Back for more food, are you?' I shook my head, as I know how dangerous it is to presume.

'I wouldn't blame you. I get the impression they don't often let you eat.'

I nodded.

'I realise you do not know me, but if she sees you now, you will be in for another beating.' The old lady nodded her head in the direction of Iris's window. The window was open now, allowing the cooling breeze into the house. I could hear a strange moaning sound coming from the bedroom, and a squeaky sort of noise.

'Why don't you slip through this gap in the fence? If you feel brave enough, there is some maize freshly cooked on the fire in my kitchen and you are welcome to have some.' I knew you should not go with strangers. We had been told at school, that they cannot be trusted, how it was not safe, how they offer food and treats to trick you. But the people I know can't be trusted either, so what did I have to lose?

I slipped through the fence and was instantly transported to another world. The garden was green and lush, with a proper lawn. In the centre stood a grove of tall Matooke trees, their branches heaving with green cooking bananas, ripe for picking. The verges adorned with wildflowers, the sort you see in the grasslands once the rainy season has arrived. The flowers gave off a sweet aroma that, if you stood still enough, would waft in and out of your nostrils. The air filled with the noise of crickets.

The busy Ugandan town and the troubles from the other side of the fence seemed a million miles away. I followed the elderly lady into her kitchen. It was smaller than Iris's, but comfortable, the walls hung with pictures of familiar cultural scenes, the mountains, the grasslands, a young woman carrying her baby close to her body. A mat lay on the floor, small and rectangular, I have seen people kneeling on them in Bwaise. The shelves too were crammed with all sorts of artefacts, small painted bowls, handmade ornaments, loose photographs of children which looked like they were taken a hundred years ago.

'Sit,' she said. I obeyed and sat in a corner on the floor.
'On the chair, child!'

Again, I obeyed, and fidgeted on the seat as my buttocks still hurt too much to sit.

'Do you sit on the floor for mealtimes?' she asked.

'Yes,' I answered. She shook her head sadly as she poured me tea. I held the cup in both hands and inhaled the smell. I had never smelt anything like it before, fresh floral scents filled my nostrils. I hastily took a mouthful, then another.

'Slow down, you shall hiccup.' she laughed, then topped up my cup. 'You have not had tea I suppose?'

'Never.' I slurped between mouthfuls.

'You know, I see a lot of what goes on next door. It is not my place to intrude on another's business, but she does not make it easy to miss.'

I nodded. There is nothing subtle about Iris.

'Who is the new boy?'

'I don't know, some relative. He arrived on Sunday.'

'Do you like him?'

I shook my head.

'I didn't think so,' she responded. 'I have children of my own, and I am a grandmother too. My grandchildren call me Jaaja, you are welcome to do the same. I know you may not believe me, but I do not get joy out of hurting small children, or beating them, or getting them to do all the work, there is time for chores in adulthood. I may not be able to do much, but I can offer you food from time to time, and I can be a shoulder to cry on.'

I am so unused to kindness I didn't know what to say.

'What's she up to now, over there?'

'I don't know. Someone is in her room.'

'Not your Taata?'

'No.'

'Such a witch, yet she gets it from two men,' she muttered to herself.

'Sorry?'

'Just talking to myself. Come now, it won't be long until she has you taking those jerry cans out. If we leave through my front door, I can walk you around the corner, so she does not suspect where you have been.'

Her hand was soft in mine, despite the wrinkles and she smelled of sweet tea and flowers from her garden. All too soon, our door came into view.

'Thank you Jaaja.'

'You are very welcome, child.' She kissed my hand and turned to leave.

Before I went inside, a man came striding out, the buttons of his shirt undone, and a thin beige jacket slung over one shoulder. He did not look at me as he hurried off.

'Child, you are early!' Iris exclaimed. She looked hot, despite the cooling breeze. The top buttons of her dress were undone, and her hair was loose from its weave.

'I ran,' I lied.

'Well go get the cans,' she barked, but without the usual venom. I knew I had walked in on something I shouldn't, but I didn't understand what it was.

Chapter Ten

Yesterday, I was late home again. Before I went inside, I plucked Iris's long cane from its special place by the latrine and handed it to her.

'What's this for?' she grunted. Her eyes were yellow, a sign she had been smoking her special tobacco.

I bent over. 'I thought I'd save you the trouble of fetching it yourself.'

She grunted and took a half-hearted swipe at my backside.

Naturally, she hadn't saved me any food. Still, the dirty plates had been left for me, so I polished off the scraps as I cleared up. Once I heard Iris snoring, I stole some posho, slicing the maize dough so carefully she wouldn't notice it had been tampered with. There was a lump of cooked meat in a bowl, covered with a cloth. I dug thin slivers of it from the underside, as much as I could get away with. I also managed to sneak a couple of mouthfuls of curry which had been covered in reserve for the following day. I longed to eat more, but I have learned to be as cunning as a hyena. This is how I have managed to survive.

That day, Mr. Joram had held me back after class, asking how I had slipped back into 'unpunctuality.' When I explained, he said, 'Just tell your auntie that you must leave the house earlier. She will understand.' What could I say? How could I describe a force of nature like Iris to a man who had never met her? After a moment or two of stuttering, he lost his patience and excused me. Farida had waited for me, showing herself a true friend, worrying that I was to get a beating. She joined me for the first part of my walk, but soon peeled off home. She said Bwaise scared her. I couldn't blame her. It scared me too.

On my walk back I cursed Mussa. He had said that morning that he was bored chasing work, that he was going to relax in front of the TV instead. Iris grumbled that he was lazy, like me, yet she hadn't made him get the water. That job was mine, as usual. He felt no obligation to do any chores, despite being a guest in the house. He was, as always, slumped in the same chair I had left him in that morning, half asleep, cans empty.

So here I am today, scanning the work tops for food. Once more, I'm grateful that the girls don't eat the crusts left over by the posho inside the pan. I'm so late this evening the house is already still. The powder Iris sprinkles on Taata's food has worked. I can hear his snores from the kitchen. The girls and Mussa are in bed too. I go to the latrine, as I hope to see a light from Jaaja's house. I had not seen her since that blissful hour in her home, although I'd heard her humming to herself as she tended her garden. Alas, her place is in darkness. I sneak behind the latrine and stick my head through the hole in the fence. My nostrils are filled with the sweet floral fragrance once more, which soothes me.

I make my way to bed. I slip out of my clothes and into my damaged nightdress. It is still torn at the back, but I found some loose fabric which works as a sash to hold it together. I climb onto my sacks, now dried out and pull my sheet up close. The moon is bright this evening. It is shining through the tiny windows, making shadows on the walls. I look to the familiar lines in the brickwork, tracing them with my finger, I am certain this one is new, a thin hairline crack branching off from the main one, tiny and insignificant. Perhaps I had simply not noticed it before? But how could I have missed it? So small, and lonely. It deserves to be noticed.

My eyelids droop with exhaustion, but before I nod off, I sense something near me. A large, black shadow blocks out the moonlight. Above me stands the figure of a man. I panic, I have heard stories like this from people in Bwaise, Men breaking into houses late at night, killing the men, taking the women and girls to be sold as slaves at a black market. I throw my sheet over my head. Has he seen me? Perhaps he has not noticed a child lying on a heap of old sacks? I plead that he has not seen me. I lie still, there are no sounds, no footsteps, no movement, but suddenly the figure closes in on me. A hand is placed over my mouth, gripping so tightly I can't scream, I can't breathe. I try and wriggle free, but I cannot move. I try and breathe through my nose, but the sheet makes it difficult. Why won't Mussa wake up? I say the words over and over in my head; Wake up, Mussa, wake up. Help me, Mussa! Maybe he is already dead? He isn't snoring. Mussa must be dead. Must I die also? Is this how I am to die?

64

His other hand is around my ankles, he yanks me towards him. My nightdress is pulled up high, around my knees, he spreads my ankles. What is happening? What is he doing to me? I try to kick but he is way too strong. Has he poisoned me? It is as though my body is shutting down. I have no strength to move, no fight in me. My legs are heavy, like rocks, I try but they will not move. There is a moment of stillness, a moment of clarity, as though I know this is it, the end. I am not ready to die. I have so much to prove, I want to show the world that I am worth something, that I can be someone. I want to show Iris that I am as good as she. That I am better than her. If I die now there will be no one at my funeral. The neighbours will say I had a sad little life, it is good that I died young as I was just a burden, I was going nowhere. Perhaps Jaaja will cry if I die? Why would they bother with a funeral? I will be thrown to the wild dogs in the wastelands. I am not ready to die.

Something hard is shoved between my legs. The pain is sharp, burning, piercing. It drives violently into me, inside my body, from where I urinate, what is happening to me? It stabs at me. Is this what death feels like? I hope this is death now. I do not want to live with this pain. I cannot live with this pain, so excruciating I want to faint. He is grunting like an animal. There is heavy breathing; a breath, then a grunt, then another breath. I try and focus on the noise, ignore the pain, ignore the pain, the agony, the agony. Is this what being stabbed is like? Please just kill me. Is there a knife inside me? I have heard about stabbings, the knife goes inside you, this must be a stabbing. As I lie awaiting my death, it is suddenly over. His throat lets out one long moan and then the hard object is gone. Have I been stabbed? His body is no longer tense, I can feel the strength diminishing. He is weakening. The hand is removed from my mouth and I whip the sheet quickly away from my face. My mouth hungry for air, I gulp at it. He still stands before me. One of my ankles in his hand. He runs one finger down the inside of my leg, from my knee, along my calf, and down to my toes. He snorts and throws my leg back onto my sack. I am still alive, and he is walking away. He walks across to Mussa's mattress. Is it his turn now? I try to call out, to warn Mussa, but then I understand. The man is not just a man. There is no intruder. He is Mussa.

Chapter Eleven

The bleeding is bad. I hurt in a place where I didn't know pain like this could exist. I am burning down there. I feel like I am on fire, but no flames appear. Every movement makes my body flinch. The dawn is coming so I will have to get up, but I can't. If I could make it down the hallway, I could wake Taata quietly, so Iris doesn't stir, and tell him what has happened. But I don't dare risk waking Mussa, the Devil man. He sleeps so peacefully now.

The sunlight has begun breaking through the early morning clouds and I know I must get up. As I look down in the dim light, I can see a pool of bright red staining what is remaining of my nightdress. It has seeped through onto my thread-bare sheet. Iris will be angry. I may just have time to clean it before she wakes. I should tell her. I should just tell her. This shouldn't have happened. *I* didn't put the blood there, he did. He should not be in this house. He should not be near me, or the other girls. He is a monster, if he has done this to me will he do it to the others too? Will she risk her own children?

It is time to move. I raise my head and my stomach churns. I feel sick with the pain. I claw at the wall, my nails feel for the cracks and I dig them in, using them for leverage and pull myself to my knees. I am once again thankful they are there. I feel a warmth on my thighs and am certain I am bleeding again. My throat tightens as I attempt to contain my sobbing. As I get to my feet, my insides feel as though they'll fall out. I feel heavy between my legs, full. Maybe he did stab me. Maybe he cut my intestines when he was up there. We had learnt about intestines in school, long wriggly things, where your urine comes from. What if I'm about to spill my guts? Maybe I am to die after all, just a slow torturous death - first my intestines will fall, then my kidneys, my liver, my heart. They will fall out one by one with me standing here, watching. Will the pain get worse? How long until I die?

My legs are shaking, as are my arms, I lean against my wall as I make my slow break for the door. I drag my feet. Mussa stirs in his corner. I hold my breath in dread, but then he rolls over, settles again. The family are still asleep. All the bedroom doors are shut as I shuffle along the corridor. The house is at peace.

I fumble with the back-door lock. I wish I could go to Jaaja. I jimmy open the door and fall into the cold dawn air. I start to breathe again. I move to the cold latrine and try to see what he has done to me. Why do I hurt so much? Do I look different? Am I cut? Why all the blood? It is dark in the latrine, only a few holes in the wood where sun beams fight their way through. Beams that come into this horrible, smelly, drab cabin to die. Today the light is not strong enough to break through the gaps and knot holes, so I can't see the damage that has been done. I want to pee, but I am afraid of the pain. I dig my nails into my own clammy, pink palms. I cry out when I urinate. I can't help it. There's a stinging, like alcohol on a flesh wound. I sob so much I can't breathe. I'm suffocating once again. The air in the latrine is stale, wretched, stagnant. At last it's over. I sob for my mother. I cry her name over and over. I want her more now than I ever have. What would she do if she heard this man had hurt me in such a way? I picture her holding me in her arms, stroking my hair, kissing my brow. She would tell me it is going to be ok. She would get the devil that hurt me, he would never again hurt anyone. She will lock him up, she will hurt him like he hurt me. And what of my father? He and his friends would drag Mussa into the streets. They would beat him, light a fire and burn him, like they did to that man in Bwaise. Mussa's crime is much worse.

I want my Maama. I hear the back door swing open. I halt my sobs immediately, my ears listening for movement.

'Lela, you in there? Hurry, you have chores.' It is Iris, the house is awake.

I try and stop the tears but panic, how can I go inside like this? I can hear the door creak shut again. I peek through a crack in the peeling wood. She has gone inside.

I tell myself I am strong, that I can do anything. I control my breathing. My eyes are puffy and stinging. I use some of the rags kept in the latrine to stem the bleeding and walk slowly to the house, glancing back for a moment at Jaaja's home. I am tempted to just slip through the gap in the fence and hide amongst the matooke trees. As I pull the back door closed behind me, I can hear voices in the kitchen. Iris and Mussa. He is acting as though nothing has happened. I clutch my torn, bloody nightdress in my fists. She looks at me, a question in her eyes, and glances at Mussa, who continues gathering food for his breakfast.

'Iris.' My voice quivers. I must be strong in his presence. 'Iris, I must talk to you.'

'Oh, must you?'

'Please.' Iris throws down a knife and walks out of the kitchen, I am expected to follow. She leads me into her bedroom. My eyes scan the room for Taata, but he is gone, I had not heard him leave. I wish he were here.

'So?' She raises her eyebrows, the 'so' heavily laden with sarcasm. I clear my throat.

'He hurt me, Iris.' I lift my nightdress slightly to draw her attention to the blood stains.

She gasps, but quickly contains herself. 'What did he do?' I avert my eyes. I am not sure I can bring myself to speak of it out loud.

'He, umm, he came to my bed, last night, he stabbed me with... with.' I can't say any more. I raise my eyes to meet hers. She does not look concerned. She folds her arms and waits for me to say more. I do not understand; this doesn't happen to the other girls? Or does it? They have never mentioned it? Is this not something bad? It felt so bad, so wrong, why is she not angry? Then suddenly she erupts like a volcano.

'You are accusing him to make my family look bad. You probably encouraged him, daughter of a whore as you are.'

This is a word I do not understand, but fear I am to hear more often. I cry fresh tears.

'Stupid girl. Do I look like I care? For goodness' sake stop hanging around in that blood-stained rag. Go and clean yourself up.'' She barges her heavy body past me and returns to the kitchen.

I can't help but cry, I know I should just get on with things, dress, clean up the blood and continue with my normal chores, but *I* care. *I* care about what he has done to me. I am a person. I am someone. I cry quietly this time, alone, in Iris's bedroom.

She realises I'm still there and marches back. 'Child, get out of my room, dress and get the girls ready for school.' She looks at the spot where I stand, above drops of blood which have dripped onto her floor. She swears, then, as if a switch has been flicked. She is infuriated, like a raged bull. If her skin was not so dark, I am certain she would turn red.

'Clean that filth off my floor. Stop snivelling. Get dressed. It's time you realised that you're only good for one thing.' She drags me towards the back door leaving a trail of blood droplets behind me. Caroline stands at the top of the hallway, her eyes like saucers.

'Get to that latrine, clean yourself up and get dressed. Do you understand me?' she throws the door of the latrine open and places me heavily upon it.

'No, Iris, don't,'

She rummages through a pile of tools Taata keeps in a corner near the house. She pulls out a length of rough rope. She pins me down against the latrine. She works quickly, twisting the rope around my ankles, my body, my hands, then the other end under the latrine. I fight furiously, but she's too strong for me.

'You will stay there until you stop that filthy bleeding.'

'I won't stay here.' I shout back, outraged at being locked in the stinking latrine. She takes off her head scarf and stuffs it into my mouth, I shake my head violently, but she knots it tightly at the back of my head, smiles and slams the latrine door shut behind her. I am gagged, alone, tied to a latrine. I want to die.

I must have passed out. When I awake the sun is high overhead and the air in the latrine reeks. My head is throbbing. I am parched. The heat is ferocious, and everything hurts. I fight the urge to retch for fear of choking. I try to wriggle free, but Iris has tied her knots well. Is she aware that I had passed out? Has she checked on me since she left me here? It has been hours. It feels like noon, going by the heat radiating from the shack. I'm astonished to find that I'm hungry. My life has disintegrated, but for my stomach, it's business as usual.

I want to rest some more, I feel weaker by the second, there is nowhere to lay my head. The walls are too far to reach. I try to slouch and rest my chin on my chest, but it's already hard enough to breathe. My only hope is Jaaja. I listen carefully, is she humming in her garden? Had she heard any of the shouting this morning, does she know I am in here? I can raise my feet just a few inches from the ground, enough to stomp on the floor. It is not loud, but if she is in her garden, she may hear it. I do it again and again. The splintered wood grates at my heels, but I am already in so much pain, and I am desperate. I hear a noise, not far away, and stop to listen. I take my chances and start banging once more. Then I hear her voice.

'Lela?' A whisper, from behind me, Jaaja.

'Humm, mmmm,' My words are muffled beyond recognition, so I simply bang harder. I can hear a struggle behind me. I know Jaaja would not be able to fit through the gap in the fence, I suspect she is breaking more of the wood away. I have stopped banging now and I am tense, frozen to the seat. I hope Iris can't hear the noise of the fence being splintered. Jaaja's voice is closer now.

'Lela, child, are you in there?' I call through the headscarf and she hears my muted voice. The door is pulled open, and I'm blinded by a sudden rush of sunlight. I turn my head away until my eyes adjust.

'Child! Allah, what have they done to you this time?' She removes the gag from my mouth. I cough as the outside air hits my dry throat. I am desperate for water.

'Please, please,' I beg. I do not know entirely what I am pleading for, for her to rescue me, take me away from this place, for her simply not to be caught helping me. Her fingers are nimble for an elderly lady and I am soon free, but when I try to stand my feet fail me. She takes my arm and drapes it around her shoulders to help carry my weight. All is still from the house. She eases me gently from the stall and props me in the shade behind it.

'I am going through the fence. Ok, Lela? Then I shall pull you through.'

Jaaja slowly lowers herself down to my height, and then onto her hands and knees. My body feels tense, I dare not move, certain we are going to be caught. I wish Jaaja could move faster, but it takes a lot of effort for her to get through the gap, even now it has been widened. At last she is through and, although shaking, I manage to edge nearer to the fence. She uses all her strength to pull my body through. Once I have reached the lush green grass, I sink into it alongside her. Both of us are too exhausted to speak.

At last she rises and fetches a hammer and taps a few pins into the wood she removed.

'It won't be long before they come looking for you. I do not want them to suspect you are here.'

'Jaaja, I can't go back, please don't make me.' She slowly puts her hammer down and looks at me, her eyes sad. She studies my face, I watch her study my cracked lips, then her eyes trace their way down the outline of my body to the blood stains. She does not respond, but gently pulls me to my feet. I stagger into her kitchen. The air is much cooler in here and I relax as I rest my head on her table. She pours me a glass of water, which I quickly swallow, then another. She prepares me a chapati.

'Come, you must eat child.' I stare at the chapati.

'Please, Jaaja, he hurt me, I will tell you what he has done, what they have done, please don't make me return to them.'

'Lela,' she pulls a chair closer and sits alongside me. 'You do not need to tell me what has been done to you.'

I stare at the dried blood around my ankles. Should I expect these things to happen to me? Am I naive in thinking that they shouldn't?

'Lela, I wish you could stay here with me, I really do,' I glance at her hopefully, but I know what is to come next. 'But, you can't my dear. Iris is a difficult woman; she would make things very hard for both you and me if she found out you were here.'

'But she says I am a *Bastard*, that she hates me. Surely, she should be happy to see the back of me.'

'Child, I am saddened that you will have to return.' She holds my chin with her soft wrinkled hand. 'Please eat.' I take a small bite from the chapati she offers me. From the other side of the fence I hear my name.

'Lela, Lela, where are you, *mbwagwe*?' Iris. My heart lurches in fright. Jaaja pulls her finger sharply to her mouth.

72

Iris bangs on the latrine walls and then searches around the stark garden. Both of us stare at the patched-up hole in the fence, but she does not notice it.

Iris heads back indoors and I am in tears again. The thought of returning is too much. I can't bear the beating I will get when I am home again. The thought of sleeping in that room with that monster makes me sick to my stomach.

'Come here, child,' Jaaja pulls me close to her. I can smell the flowers from her garden on her skin. She smells of life, of freedom, of comfort. It is the sort of smell I have imagined on my mother. It makes me cry harder. Jaaja holds me tighter.

'What about your Taata? When does he get home? He is kind to you.'

I sniffle, 'I don't know, usually when I am fetching the water. I don't think he is well; he sleeps a lot.'

'If I was married to that, I would want to sleep all the time too,' I hear Jaaja mutter under her breath, 'Listen. You need to go home, but we shall wait at the front, until you see Taata return home. She will not beat you while he is there.' I nod.

'I expect I will still be sent out for water.'

'If that is so, then you need your strength, so eat.' She pushes the chapati at me again. I do not argue and take another bite.

Jaaja washes and stitches my nightdress. When the sun dips towards the horizon, she walks me to the front of the row of houses and we sit under the shade of a tree, the branches drooped low, so we are sure Taata won't notice us. He pulls up and walks slowly towards the front door, still in a hypnotic state.

'Good luck, my child,' she whispers, pulling me close, 'Come to me in the morning.'

'But I can't. I must go to school; I am already late every day. The later I am the more my teacher beats my knuckles.'

'I know, but you can ride to school with my granddaughter. She goes to school in Bwaise too but takes a boda-boda every morning. You can ride with her, then you'll be safe, and you won't be late.' She kisses my forehead and then turns slowly to return home. She looks worn out. She may not be able to take me in, but what she has done means more to me than she can ever know.

'Hello, my girl, I have missed you,' Taata greets me with warmth. He ruffles my hair, 'Why are you in your nightgown? Were you sick today, my love?'

Iris stares at the starched white of my nightgown, whilst Mussa is behind me.

'Sort of.' I respond as Iris circles me from a distance, her eyebrows raised.

'Well she is better now,' Iris comments, her teeth gritted as she speaks, dangling a jerry can from her right hand.

'If she has been sick, she shouldn't do the water tonight,' says Taata.

'She will do as she is told.'

'Or what? Will the Shadow Man come and get me while I'm sleeping?' I glare at Iris, confident with Taata by my side. She looks away first.

'You know those stories are not real, my love.'

I so badly want to tell him. Iris looks deeply uncomfortable. This has been enough of a victory for now. I snatch the jerry cans from her and give her another look. I am not broken yet. I fetch her the water, though it pains me. I tell myself that Taata loves me, that Jaaja loves me. That I am worth something, that I am not nothing, I am not a nobody. I sleep fitfully, on my sacks, free of attack, for one night at least.

74

Chapter Twelve

A week or so later, he waited for me late one evening after my trip to the pump. The room was dark as I snuck in, his bed covers ruffled, leading me to think he was in them. Instead he lurked behind the door, jumping me as I walked through. He grabbed me as he closed the door, hurrying to remove his belt and push me to the mattress. Knowing what to expect did not make it hurt any less. I fought with all my strength, biting chunks from his hand, determined to escape, but his strength proved too much for me. He pressed my face deep into his bedsheets to muffle any noise. I pleaded with him to stop, I screamed for Taata as he thrust against my body, tearing me again.

'Shut up, you Bastard. You'd better get used to this,' he grunted as he used me, holding my hair tightly in his fist.

His visits became horrifyingly regular. Not only was my bed not safe, nowhere else in the house was safe either. He would always wait for Taata to leave, but then anywhere was fair game to him. He caught me once on my way out of the latrine, pushing me back in as I opened the door, leaning me over so he couldn't see my face. Saturdays were always the worst. Taata would have errands to run and work to do, the other girls would leave to play with their friends. Iris always had her man visitor these days. They would close her bedroom door for hours. I would do my chores with just the sound of laughter echoing down the hall. I knew now what the grunting meant, but she did not hate and fear it as I did. She welcomed that man with open arms. With the house all but empty on Saturdays, Mussa switched job hunting for Lela hunting. I fought with every ounce of my energy. His arms now covered in the scars from my nails and teeth, but I could never stop him.

He often pushed me against the living room wall, pressing my ear so I could hear the noises from Iris's room. He warned me not to make a sound or Iris and her man would come out, and then it would be his turn too. The fear of that was enough to make me shut up.

Sometimes I would plead with her to make him stop. Her response depended on her mood. Often, she accused me of lying. 'You are making it up. He is a lazy good-for-nothing, but even he would not touch a filthy ragdoll like you.' Or, she would assume I was asking for it. 'It is not his fault you give him the eye. You are just like your mother. Good for only one thing. Better that you learn that now.' My crying and pleading did nothing to move her. I tried a different tack.

'I will tell Taata about your visitor.'

'What visitor?'

I looked at her, incredulous. Did she think I was blind?

'The man who visits you when he is away.'

She puffed herself up to twice her size, and her face darkened with a furious temper. She smacked me so hard across the ear that I fell on to the floor. She picked me up and pulled my face so close to hers that I could smell the egg on her breath. 'If you tell him, I will *kill* you. Do you understand?' Looking into those enraged, bloodshot eyes, I believed her.

I have become numb now. Mussa shows no signs of leaving or starting work. I think about my mother always these days. I am sure she is still alive somewhere. I think about what I will tell her if we ever meet. How Iris invited this fiend into her home, willfully blind to his attacks. I picture her rage, perhaps she is with my father. He would come and find Iris, then Mussa, he would have him killed, I know he would, and I would be allowed to be a child again. I think about this as he uses me then throws me aside like a dog when he is finished. I am thinking about it now, as I sweep the kitchen floor, Mussa and Iris staring at me from the chairs. They talk quietly amongst themselves, but I still hear them.

'Does she still cry, when you visit her?' Iris asks him.

He looks uncomfortable, but he answers, 'No, not for a long time.'

'She needs to learn that it's all she's good for.'

She glares at me as I work in the far corner, picking up the scraps from the floor. 'I should write to her mother, tell her what a whore her daughter is.' My sweeping has slowed, I cannot risk not hearing what is said. She speaks of my mother as a person who is alive. My heart leaps at the thought that I may be able to find her. Did Iris say write to her? Is there an address somewhere? I try not to show my excitement. Iris throws her cleaning rag at me. The conversation is over, but I've heard enough to make up my mind.

I head to bed early, as Mussa is out. I am just settling under my sheet when the door bursts open. It is clear he has been at the liquor. He stumbles over his own feet and lands harshly on the concrete floor. He swears, and I can't help but snigger.

'Shut up 'mbwa',' he spits.

I turn my back to him. He grasps my shoulder and turns me to face him.

'What gives you the right to laugh at me? You are a nobody.' He clumsily unbuttons his trousers. I kick and bite, then brace myself. Straightening every limb, stiffening my body. He struggles to open my legs, digging his nails into my skin to grip them. I do not relax my muscles. I stare at the ceiling and picture reuniting with mother once more. He gives up, my strength overpowering his, at last, pulls himself away from me and spits on me.

'Not worth it.' He sneers then passes out on his mattress. It is a small win for me.

I sleep well that night. Mussa's snores reassure me that he is out for the count. Nothing wakes me until the first light of dawn starts creeping in. I rise quickly, with a new-found lust for life. Under my sack is my school outfit and the only other dress I own. I quickly put my school clothes on and hide my spare under the elastic of my skirt, tucking in my shirt to flatten all evidence of it. I clear the remnants of supper away and prepare breakfast as normal, smiling sweetly at each of the girls as they enter, wishing Iris a good morning. She simply glares, never one to cope well with mornings. I take a large handful of food from her plate and shove it into my mouth, right under her nose as Taata enters. She looks at me in disbelief. Taata pulls me to him.

'You are jolly today my girl, I like to see you happy.' He draws me closer to him to whisper, 'I have seen so little of it of late.' I give him an extra squeeze around his waist, and for a moment I am saddened. He deserves a better life too. I turn quickly to hide my face, gathering the girl's school bags. I steal all their lunch money. It is time to go.

As I have done for the last few weeks I wait until Iris has gone back inside and Taata has driven off with the girls, then I sneak around the block to Jaaja's. She is waiting with the boda-boda, as always with a small parcel of chapati and fruit for me in her hand. She looks relieved to see me. I run, as I always do, but instead of climbing in behind the motorcycle I quickly throw my arms around her.

'Thank you, thank you for everything.' She looks me in the eye and smiles a sad, tired smile. She knows, and she doesn't try and stop me.

'Wait!' she instructs the driver and goes back inside for a minute. She comes back with some money for me.

'It's not much, but it's all I have in the house right now. I will miss you Lela, good luck.'

Tears spring to my eyes. 'Thank you, Jaaja.'

'Goodbye, my child.'

I'm too choked to speak. I watch her until we turn the corner. I expect it is the last time I will ever see her. She and Taata have shown me the only kindness I have ever known.

Chapter Thirteen

It is a funny feeling sitting behind that motorcycle driver, watching the streets whizz past. I have pictured my moment of escape so many times before, imagining my elation, but the reality is quite different. Despite everything, I feel an odd sensation of sadness. I'm leaving the only life I know. Iris and Mussa are monsters, but Taata showed me love, even the girls had their moments. Part of me wants to see Iris's face when she realises that there is no one to fetch the water, or help cook and clean, or accompany her to the latrine when she wants to go and smoke for an hour in the middle of the night. She will never balance a jerry can on her head in the sweltering heat, exhausted, and ask herself how she could have forced this duty on such a young child for so many years. A woman like Iris will never change. She will pass the work on to someone else. Mussa will bear the brunt of it now. I can only hope so, I think viciously.

The boda-boda drops me outside school and I wave goodbye to Jaaja's granddaughter for the final time. I am early. Since Jaaja let me use the boda-boda I am often early. I shift my skirt slightly to rearrange the dress I have hidden underneath. I am proud of myself for making such a seamless getaway, but now I am unaware of what my next move will be. I shall attend school as normal, but then what? I have been in Bwaise long enough now not to be so terrified of it. In fact, these days there are often people to wave at, or smile to; the same children that play in the street each day, the man that sells chapati… but that doesn't mean I wish to be one of the children on the street when it gets dark. I have seen them sheltering from the rain, finding old sacks to sleep in on the side of the road. My money will not go far, and I have nowhere to go. I fear I have not thought this through properly.

Farida arrives. She has become my only friend, although she still knows so little about me. I have not told her about the horrors of my life. When we are together, I want to play, not burden her with my troubles.

As school ends, she has more questions. 'You are not rushing today? Are you not needed at home?' I consider my reply carefully.

'I am not going home today.' I stare at the ground and carelessly kick a small pebble from one foot to the other.

'Why not? Won't your auntie miss you?'

'I don't expect so; she is a witch.' Farida laughs at this, which makes me smile too. Even describing Iris as a witch lifts the knotted feeling from the pit of my stomach. It feels good to speak the truth to someone else.

'Why is she a witch?'

'Well, she smokes this pipe, late at night. I have seen her lock herself in the latrine and mumble these crazy words to herself, like that old woman we saw. She sprinkles powder on my uncle's food too. She says it is to help him sleep but he always seems sick afterwards. Sometimes she invites men round, they go into her room when Taata is not there. They get up to… things.'

'You mean… sex?'

'You know about sex?'

'Yes, my sister told me about it. It sounds disgusting.'

I couldn't agree more.

'So where will you go if you don't go home?'

'I don't know, but I can't go back. She beats me, and she invited this evil man, Mussa to stay, and he hurts me too. My Taata is kind, but he is never there and can't protect me. I have heard them talk of my mother. They say I am a bastard, but I have heard them speak of her as though she is alive. I want to find my mother, she will protect me and look after me, I know she will.'

The more I talk about it the more emotional I become. I realise I am crying. She stares at me, but with concern and kindness.

'You will come home with me, maybe my mother can help you, my mother is kind, she will not like to hear that you have been hurt.'

'You… you don't think she will mind?'

'No, my sisters are older and have left home now, it is only me and her, and my father, but he works a lot, I think

80

she gets lonely just me and her, I think she will like the company.'

Farida takes my hand. I am too overwhelmed to respond, and I simply follow as she leads me down various Bwaise streets until we get closer to her home. I am excited to meet her mother, but nervous too. Farida tells me she is a kind woman but in my experience many people are not what they seem. I am so used to being unwanted. I can't bear the thought of not being welcomed by Farida's mother. I pause for a moment, but Farida pulls me excitedly towards her house.

'Maama, Maama!' She is calling before I have the chance to speak again.

'Hello, my child.' A small woman appears from behind a beaded curtain, she is dressed in a bright yellow cloth, her hair wrapped in matching material. She isn't much taller than me, but she has an older face. Wrinkles surround her eyes and they crease as she smiles at me. She reaches a soft hand to stroke my cheek.

'Farida, you did not tell me you were bringing a guest home tonight. I would have cleaned up more, who is this pretty girl?'

'This is my friend Lela from school, Maama. She needs somewhere to stay; may she stay with us?'

'Lela, where is your maama?'

'I don't know.'

'Your father?'

'I have been living at my auntie and uncle's.'

'Well, won't they miss you?'

'No, my auntie does not love me, she is a witch, please don't make me go back there.' The panic is easily detected in my voice, I can feel my heart start to race, I had felt so proud leaving this morning, it had felt the right thing to do. Now I realise I can easily be forced to return.

Farida's maama is studying my face; she still does not seem angry or upset with me, just sad. She gently reaches out to me again. This time I flinch, worried she will drag me back to Iris, but she takes my hand in hers, and signals for me to come in.

Once inside she remains quiet. Farida watches her mother. I suspect the silence is unusual. She moves around the kitchen, filling a pot with water and then setting it to boil. Eventually, as the water begins to bubble, she leans the palms of her hand against the tabletop and looks at me.

'Lela, please come, sit by me here.' I hesitate. I am scared she will tell me what I can't bear to hear. 'Trust me, Lela.'

Farida takes my hand and gently pulls me closer to the table.

'Lela, I can tell you are scared. I want you to tell me why you think your auntie is a witch, and then I will try and help you. Please tell me your story, Lela.'

I think carefully about what to say. If I do not tell the whole truth, then she will no doubt think I should go back, and I may be beaten for being disrespectful of kindness. But if I tell them everything then Farida and her family may regard me differently. I can't bear their pity, and even worse, their disgust.

'I do not know my mother,' I begin, 'I lived with my auntie since I was a baby, for a long time I thought she was my mother, but she never treated me with kindness. Eventually she called me Bastard and beat me, and made me do all the chores; fetching water, cooking, cleaning. I was allowed no friends. One day I could go to school and I thought things would be better, but they got worse. I was beaten at school and at home. She invited a man to stay in my room and he, he,' I couldn't describe it, I stared at my feet, ashamed that I had let this happen to myself, I wish I had been stronger. 'Well, he hurt me.'

Her hand meets her mouth and I realise she understands what I mean.

'You poor child.' She touches my shoulder lightly but as I flinch, she removes her fingertips.

'Tell her what you told me, about the witch lady.' Farida encourages.

'She puts powder on my uncle's food. She says it helps him sleep but he is always sick afterwards. She also goes out to the latrine late at night and smokes green stuff in a pipe and mumbles words to herself repeatedly, like some crazy woman. When my uncle is not there, she invites men round and they lock themselves in her room for hours...' I stop, it is all too raw, too soon to speak of it. I do not want to think about them. I do not want to think about Taata alone in that house. I see the other girls becoming more like their mother by the day, Josephine especially. It is only a matter of time before Taata is in a house full of witches, I do not think he will survive it.

Farida's mother returns to the stove and makes us a hot drink. She pours it into two mugs and hands one to me.

'Thank you. Farida said her mother was kind.'

'Please, call me Hajat, Lela, we will not hurt you here, you are safe.'

Safe. Safe. Safe. I repeat the word over and over in my head. The warming drink soothes the anxious knots in my stomach. The agony of worry dissipates slightly, and I look around my surroundings. Hajat is cooking now, pilau rice with rich spices envelop the room. Farida draws something on some scrap papers across the table. The kitchen is small, and more basic than Iris's, but it feels comforting. There are family photos of Farida as a baby, held close by doting parents. Children's drawings adorn the walls; Farida's doll takes pride of place at the head of the table. I admire it, it is dressed in bright fabric, like the material in Hajat's dress. The clothing has been stitched well, with care, as has the doll itself, plump little arms at horizontal angles from an equally plump body. Two wide black eyes and a black hand-stitched smile on the brown cloth. I like it so much, but I dare not touch something that is not mine.

'You can play with her if you want.' Farida has been watching me.

'Oh no, she is beautiful, I couldn't.'

'Please, Maama made her, I know you will take good care.' She stands up and walks over to the doll, then picks her up and hands her to me, I tentatively take her, my fingertips trace the outline of her face, the smile, the eyes. I finger the cotton fabric.

'You are very lucky,' I can't help but say it.

'I know.' Farida shrugs as she continues drawing.

'Girls,' says Hajat. 'It is time we made Lela a bed. For now, there is to be no more terror in your life. You can be a child here. You are to play; you are to relax.'

That night I sleep on that soft mattress, in that soft bed, more soundly than I ever have done before.

Chapter Fourteen

My time with Farida, Hajat, and her father, Haji, are the happiest days of my life. Farida and I are never given heavy chores. I always have food. I am never late for school and I wear clean dresses every day. I have begun to realise however, that my time is coming to an end. Haji has asked me a lot about my family, names that I may remember, people that came to stay while I was at Iris's. I see him and Hajat whispering to each other too. I knew that my time here was never going to be permanent, and their kindness only makes me long all the more for my own mother. I used to cry for her at Iris's, I pictured her so many times caring for me and loving me. Hajat has shown me that motherly love really does exist. She has treated me like her own daughter. I long for answers. I am desperate to understand how she could have given me up to Iris. She wouldn't have done it unless she had to, surely?

The rainy season has arrived, and Farida and I are sheltering inside after school, playing with a pair of dolls made from banana fibre. Hajat had helped us make them after seeing my love for Farida's doll. They are not so expertly crafted, and much smaller, but the one I hold in my hand is mine. The first toy I have ever owned. Her face painted onto the fibre, a slightly crooked smile, wonky nose and tiny dots for eyes, but she looks friendly. What I love most is her dress. Hajat had found a tiny scrap of fabric left over from her own dress and we had stuck it to the banana doll, it bunches out in places, but I love that most of all, it makes her look like she is permanently twirling in the wind.

Haji rushes through the kitchen door, brushing the large raindrops from his jacket. Farida runs to give her father a warm embrace. Despite their huge kindness, I know that is not my place. Hajat looks eagerly at her husband, an unspoken question hangs in the air and he nods once to answer. Hajat calls me forward.

'Lela, there is someone here to speak to you.' I feel nervous suddenly. I trust them, they have kept me safe, but I am fearful of who will walk through that door. A tall stranger enters. He shakes off an umbrella before he closes the door behind him.

'Lela, sweetheart, this man has come to speak to you about your mother.'

'I told you, I do not know my mother.'

'Would it be alright for him to just ask a few questions?' Haji asks. I hold my small wooden doll tightly in my hand and approach the man. He holds out his hand to shake mine, like I have seen adults do. I am surprised, but I offer him my hand in return. He directs me to the table, and I sit down beside him, Haji joins us too, but Farida is steered out of the room by her mother.

'Lela, I would like to ask you about your mother.'

Nothing has changed, why must they keep asking me?

Haji urges me on gently, 'Lela, we know you don't know much about her, just tell the gentleman what you told me.' Repeating my sorry story will not help me know who she is any more than I do now.

'I do not know her, I always lived with Iris. Iris spoke like she was alive, but I don't think I ever met her.'

'Did a lady called Maria ever visit you?' I think. There had been so many visitors over the years. Maria's face suddenly appears in my mind.

'Yes, she did visit, not so long ago, just before I started school, Iris said she was my auntie, does she know my mother?'

'Lela, I believe I know who your mother is, and where to find her. If you feel ready, I would like to take you to her.' He seems honest, but I am nervous. Haji places his warm hand over mine, drawing my eyes back to him.

'I shall come with you Lela, so you feel safe, to make sure you are happy.' Was this really happening? Could it really be as easy as this?

Farida appears at the kitchen door. She has been listening to our conversation. She looks excited, a wide smile lights up her face.

'Lela,' She carefully approaches the table, 'Your own mother, just like you always wanted.' Her eyes sparkle, more, I think, than my own. I think about all the pain that I have been through, to think that I could have simply left and stayed with Farida, and my mother would be found in a matter of weeks? It just doesn't seem feasible for such a difficult story to end so suddenly, so happily.

'I - I would like to meet her.' I eventually say, 'but please Haji, come with me, I am worried.'

'I understand.'

Hajat enters the room carrying a small bag. She has collected my belongings. I realise there is much more in the bag than my simple dress. She has added some of Farida's clothes. I try to refuse them.

'We want you to know that we shall always be thinking of you. They are to remind you of your time with us.'

'Thank you, I shall never forget your kindness.' I clutch the bag tightly and hold it close, for the first time I feel I have things that I can treasure, not just the possessions in this bag, but the happy memories that have formed in the days I have been here. I feel sure that this 'holiday' is just the start of many happier times.

I hug Hajat and Farida and climb into the back of the tall gentleman's car. He straps me in safely. This itself is a novelty. Farida stands close to her mother at the back door, Hajat's arms around her shoulder. I watch them as they disappear, imagining it is my mother holding me by my shoulders. Soon Lela, very soon.

We drive for a while. The men are silent as we slow down. Is this her home? Eventually, the car comes to a standstill and we are parked alongside a large house, in a wealthy area. The house has whitewashed walls, and pretty plants growing up one side. The gentleman knocks and another, equally tall gentleman welcomes us inside.

'So, your name is Lela?' I nod. I wonder if this is my Father?

'Come, let me introduce you to the girls, this is Ada,' an older girl, almost a teenager gives me a small smile, 'and this is Hope.' Hope is about four. 'And finally, this is Juliet.' Despite the nervous fluttering which has developed in my stomach, I can't help but grin at Juliet, a chubby baby showing off tremendous dimples on her squidgy thighs. I immediately soften at the sight of her. Ada is instructed to serve me some of the food which is cooking on the stove. I eat politely. The two weeks at Farida's have helped me to resist the temptation to shovel down any meal put in front of me. The kitchen is large, a wooden dresser stands along one wall, filled with plates and pots and pans, enough to cook for half the village. The room is silent as they watch me eat. Afterwards Ada takes me to wash and freshen up from my journey as the men talk in hushed tones from the kitchen, then Haji explains he is to return home. I wave him off, so grateful for everything he has done, but I suddenly feel very alone.

'Come, Lela,' I am seated in a large, comfortable chair in the main room. It's the most beautiful room I have ever seen. Large soft chairs decorated in floral material; the walls are covered in flowers too. Still the girls remain quiet, I dare not ask where my mother is. I suspect we're waiting for her. My palms feel sweaty and my mouth is dry. I wipe my palms on my dress, hoping the others do not see. A few moments later a door opens, and I see the face of Maria. What is she doing here? Does she know my mother? She does not smile at me as she once did, her head shakes at the sight of me. Then she walks the length of the room, staring at the man who welcomed me into the house.

'It's ok, I know, I know. She is welcome, I do not mind.' The man says softly to her, and her face calms, although her eyes look angry. My own eyes dart quickly from him, to her. It suddenly makes sense, how her visit coincided with my starting school, perhaps it was her visit that finalised it all, her money? How could she leave me there though, when she was doing so well here? How can she be my mother, how can she have come to visit me and not taken me home with her? She does not want me either, why did I come? I want to return with Haji, but he has already left. After all these years I fear Iris is right. No one wants me.

I want to say I'm sorry I came, but I can't speak. I struggle to climb out of the soft furnishings, but he stops me from moving.

'No, Lela, it is ok, I know, I know.' I am not exactly sure what he knows. I want to know too, as I feel as if I know nothing. He coaxes me back to my seat. Ada watches us closely. Maria does not take her eyes from me.

The man points at Maria. 'Do you recognise this lady?'

'Yes, she visited Iris in Lubiji.'

'This is your mother, Lela, and while I am not your real father, I want you to think of me that way. You can call me Taata now, I will look after you.' I look about the room. They are the words I have wanted to hear for so long, but I am still uneasy.

'Lela, we are family.' My new Taata smiles at me, and I smile back. He seems kind, like the Taata I left behind at Iris's. My mother I am not so sure of.

We are dismissed to begin getting ready for bed, I follow the girls, take their lead, but as I pass the kitchen my mother calls me in. I stand in front of her and look at her. She stares back at me for a moment, neither of us speaking. I want her so badly to take me in her arms like real mothers do and tell me she loves me, that she is sorry she left me with Iris. She moves towards the stove and picks up a long wooden spoon. She taps me with it; hard short taps, directly on the centre of my head.

'Why did you come here, hmm? Why do you ruin everything? Every arrangement we had, why?' I don't answer. All I can do is stare straight ahead of me, trying to remain strong as every image of motherly love evaporates. My mother's arms lovingly wrapped around me was a wonderful dream, but it was just that, a dream that I now must wake up from. There will be no heroine in my story. Unless I become my own.

Chapter Fifteen

I have been wondering if my life will always follow the same path. At Iris's it seems I was bullied by an overbearing female 'role model' yet loved by a gentle male. Here, at my mother's house, history is repeating itself. My new Taata wakes before work and hugs me, helps me to get ready for school and talks to me just like the other girls. I have learnt that the baby is his daughter, but I'm not sure of the others, and do not feel it is my place to ask. However, my mother treats the others better than I. She tells me often that I have ruined things for her, that I should have stayed with Iris. Despite her venom, I know full well I am better off here. There is no fetching water, no late-night visits from Mussa, no crazy women smoking in latrines.

I am preparing breakfast on a Monday morning when I hear the knock. It is the knock that I have come to listen for. Kasama, one of Taata's oldest friends. I run to the door.

'Hmm, now which one are you?' He lifts me up to examine my face, it has become a daily ritual. 'You must be Juliet; you are so young.'

'I am not Juliet, she is a baby, I'm a big girl.' I giggle.

'Not Juliet, you say? Then Hope? Hope is a big girl, no?'

'Not as big as me.'

'Oh well, in that case you must be Ada, she is the biggest girl of the house.' I look cross, but I am only pretending, he laughs and then so do I.

'Don't tease, Kasama.' My new Taata warns, but he is smiling.

'Ahh there he is, the big man, I heard about the promotion.' Kasama approaches Taata with his hand outstretched. Taata loses his smile, looking concerned.

'You heard?' He speaks quietly now, 'I was going to tell you myself.'

'Don't look so worried, I am happy for you, brother.' Kasama pulls Taata in for a hug, then slaps him on the back. 'This man has earned himself a promotion, Lela. He is a clever man. He works hard. You should be proud.'

I do feel proud. Neither he nor Mother had mentioned it. I am surprised. It should have been shouted from the rooftops.

Kasama sees my reaction. 'See, Big Man, don't keep it to yourself. Look how her eyes are shining.'

'I was going to tell you in person. I was worried you might be upset, as we do so much together.'

'Yeah I know, but hey, best man won and all that.'

They say goodbye to me before heading off to another job. I'm sorry to see them leave. Taata said this would be a longer job. Sometimes he is gone for days. I know he drives trucks, but that is all. I knew that this would be his last long-haul job. I had heard Mother saying how grateful she was that there would be no more travelling, that we could at last be together, properly as a family. I suppose because of the promotion. Kasama would no doubt be sad, no more long journeys with his partner.

I make myself scarce until it is time for school. I have found this is the best thing to do when Taata goes away. Mother is much more bad-tempered when he is away. She picks on me, and the other girls also get judged and ordered around. All except baby Juliet, her clear favourite. If we stay away, then she simply complains to herself. I remind myself that she does not beat me, that she has not invited a demon into the house to attack me, she does not lock me up in the latrine. I should be grateful, but I can't help wishing that she loved me like the others.

At least she loves my new Taata and is happy with him. She is not vile to him, as Iris was to my old Taata. She certainly does not invite other men to the house, no matter how long Taata is away. When they are together, he makes her laugh. I could hear her laughing as I went to sleep, snuggled up in bed, a proper bed, next to Ada. She would be laughing in the kitchen, sometimes for hours, belly laughing like baby Juliet does when you pull faces at her. Happiness to me would be my mother taking me in her arms, telling me that she loves me, that she has missed me, and that she is so pleased to have me back in her life. I long for this to happen, although I fear it never will. Despite this, on those nights when I am snuggled up in bed, my sister snoring beside me, far from Iris and Mussa, I count my blessings.

I am thinking about my role in the family as I lie in bed, late, long after Taata left for his last long-distance job. Ada is sleeping soundly, as always, and I am very aware of how quiet the house is tonight. An hour ago, Juliet stirred, and I heard Mother attend to her, I heard the gentle rhythm of a lullaby, and Mother's feet padding up and down the hall until Juliet drifted off again. I knew she was holding her, close to her chest and kissing her head between verses. I adore Juliet but can't help but feel envious, this baby getting the mother we should all have. Then a thought occurs to me. Maybe she loves Juliet because she is my new Taata's child. I wonder who *my* father is. Maybe I will never know. Maybe I shouldn't want to know.

I listen for sounds now, it has been some time since Juliet drifted back off to sleep and Mother returned to her room. There is no laughter, I suspect Mother is in bed already. She sleeps early when Taata is gone, although it is not so early now. Hours have ticked by and I am unable to sleep, my mind active as always. I hear a sound from the darkness outside, a solitary cry. I sit up and listen, it is not unusual to hear sounds late at night, we live in a town, there are often calls, barking dogs, cars, but this is different. This call had cut through the silence like a knife, some distance away, but propelled by panic. I listen for it again.

I hear it closer this time, the caller running. I can hear the vibrations in his voice with each footstep, this cry is longer, a lungful of air shrieking a single word. A single name. Maria. I am up. Mother needs to be woken. Something is very wrong. I can hear the voice getting closer, the caller is sprinting. There is no time, from my bedroom I can tell, there is no time.

I run down the hall to Mother's room and before I can knock the door is open, Mother has heard a noise but is still riddled with sleep.

'What is happening, did you call, or Juliet?' She quickly understands the noise does not come from inside the house, and she wakes, fully.

'What is that noise? No, oh no no,' Her eyes are wide, white circles against dark skin, I see them bright even in the darkness. She screams and runs down the hall, fumbling with latches, then into the street.

'Please, no, not him, please,' she cries. The runner is on our front porch now, gasping for breath. Mother does not want to hear what he has to say. The neighbours have woken, many of them standing in the street, waiting. I am cautiously nearing the front door. I have entered some sort of limbo. The world around me moves in slow motion as I await a dark fate. I can't hear everything, but I hear, 'hospital,' then mumbling, 'hurry,' more mumbling, 'no time.'

Mother struggles to compose herself. She turns to the house, pulls a coat from the hook to cover her flimsy nightdress, looks directly at me, and Ada, who is behind me, confused.

'Watch the children.' She slams the door behind her and is gone.

'What has happened, Lela? What is going on?' asks Ada. 'Taata. It's Taata isn't it?' Her eyes dart left and right in anxiety.

I nod, unable to speak. She takes my hand and we turn into the living room, knowing there will be no more sleep for us tonight. We sit down silently, both of us grateful Hope and Juliet are still asleep. I feel her warmth beside me, and I rest my head on her shoulder. She pulls me close to her. I don't speak of it, but I know she is thinking the same thing. He may not be our real father, but he is as close to one as either of us will ever get.

Chapter Sixteen

Ada and I sat side by side for hours, minds racing too much for sleep. At some point we saw the sun had risen, and watched the sky turn from black, to navy, to red. We stirred when Juliet awoke, and started preparing breakfasts, changing nappies, washing clothes. A neighbour arrived to help look after us and the younger girls seemed undisturbed by Mother's absence. Hope asked for her, but we were able to distract her with toys and food.

Then Maama returned.

It was mid-morning when we heard the front door creak. Mother, alone, her coat in her hand, her night dress bloodied. I stared at the blood stains. There were streaks of red on her shoulders, the pretty frills forever soiled. Ada and I knew better than to speak, but not Hope.

'Maama', the child called, running with outstretched arms. In a trance Mother walked past her, knocking her to the floor. She did not mean to be unkind. She simply did not see her. We stared at her, Hope shocked, until she got to her room, closing the door behind her. We heard a single desperate shriek, a cry that I will never forget, a cry that told us that Taata is dead.

Ada fell to the floor, her face in her hands. The man that had loved us all so dearly, treated us like his daughters, was gone. I tried to comfort her, but she was immobile, with no strength to move from the spot where she fell.

Hope looked from Ada, to me, and then to the room which contained our grieving Mother. The solitary shriek had since given way to helpless, heart wrenching sobbing. Hope's brow furrowed.

'What has happened Lela? Tell me, please.'

'It's Taata. He's dead.' I held my arms out to her, and she rushed into them, silent but undoubtedly crying, my tears followed.

I do not know how many hours have passed. I suspect it is supper time, but I do not feel hungry. Some of Mother's friends are here, rallying around her, but she tears away from them and shrieks like a beast as they try and console her. I watch as one tries to dab Mother's brow, now feverish with stress, but she rips the sponge away and throws it at the woman, then collapses once more. Mother's friend Beatrice is in the kitchen with Juliet, who is still full of the joys of life, not yet corrupted by death and misery. She is eating some mushed-up food and gurgling to herself as Beatrice coos at her to take another bite. She makes funny noises, but her cheeks are stained with the lines of tears, her eyes puffy and red, her lips cracked. The tears roll by themselves, uncontrollably. She stops in her tasks every now and then to pull a handkerchief from her pocket and dab at them, but to no avail, they just keep falling.

Our lives are crumbling. I loved my new Taata so much. Was I crying for the loss of a kind man? That I will never see him again? Did I cry for Mother, who has lost someone that brought her so much happiness? Did I cry for baby Juliet, who would never know her father or how good he was? Or did I cry selfishly, for myself? My future was a big dark unknown all over again. What will happen to us?

Beatrice beckons me to join her in the kitchen, I am aware that I am being given instructions, there are dishes to wash, clothes to fold. My tears blind me, but I do as I am asked. She is kind, she does not order, I feel her soft hand on my shoulder. As I fold the clothes, I come across one of Taata's shirts. It is warm from being dried in the sunshine. I hold it close. The warmth and the smell of the fabric allow me to imagine he is holding me in his arms. Beatrice sees me crying and folds me in her arms.

Then I hear Mother shouting. 'She *cannot* be mourning. He was not her Father. She is not part of this.'

Beatrice looks at me in pity. 'Shh, Lela, she doesn't mean it. I know you loved him.'

Whatever Mother says, I know that I mourn, that I must mourn, whether she likes it or not.

Chapter Seventeen

'Get up.' Mother is pulling at my bedclothes. Ada is already up. It is unusual for her to wake before me, but I have struggled with waking since Taata died. My head hurts and the only thing that makes the pain go away is sleep, so I sleep. Ada can't sleep at all. She lies awake at night, pacing our room, looking out of the window. She used to watch out sometimes when we were expecting Taata home. I wonder if she is still waiting for him. Mother stands over me, making sure I am awake. Her face is tattooed with exhaustion. Dark shadows fall under her eyes, new lines, the hair stuck to her brow suddenly greying. She throws my bedsheets down, satisfied that I am conscious enough.

Today she meets the clan. The locals, the family members, the people who will decide what place Mother has now that Taata is gone. Today we bury him. As dawn turns into morning Mother appears dressed in her bark clothes, the cloth made from the inner bark of the Mutuba tree. I catch my breath, having never seen her dressed in the cloth before. It makes her look almost regal, yet her face is still drawn. It has taken all her strength to rise today, to dress, to be brave enough to face the clan. Her concentration cannot be broken, for without it, her courage shall be broken too. We rise in her presence and bow our heads in respect. Even Hope and Juliet seem to know now is not the time to speak or giggle.

Beatrice gathers us all together, and the five of us follow Mother as she steps outside. The light appears to blind her. She hasn't left the house since she returned from the hospital, blood stained and alone. As her eyes adjust, she walks away from the happy home she has shared with my stepfather, to a dirty white car which appears to be awaiting her. Some men signal for her to get in. I do not recognise them. They do not speak. Beatrice explains that we are to follow on foot, but it's not very far. I am relieved, as I do not like the look of the men she rides with. They look stern and angry. The day is bright, the air somewhat cooler than it has been lately and I am glad of it. I breathe in deeply and feel refreshed, the overhanging headache since Taata died lifts once we are out

97

of that grief-smothered house, the air close and stagnant, heavy with depression.

By the time we reach our destination I am chattering to Hope and Beatrice. Ada remains quiet, though she has relaxed a little. She looks around the sunny streets, at the people coming and going from their homes, at the children staring at us. It is a close-knit community and they are curious. They know that Taata is gone, and that we are on the way to where he will rest. Toddlers run and play in the street, but are hushed by their parents, or moved out of our way. Death has made strangers of us.

Mother stands at the entrance to an ugly, concrete building, and watches as we approach. She no longer looks like my bad-tempered Mother. Instead, I see a little girl, scared and alone, holding a shaking hand out to her oldest friend for reassurance.

Beatrice passes Juliet to me, her body heavy as she has dozed on our stroll. I droop her over my shoulder and follow as Beatrice takes Mother's arm. She is too shaky to walk unaided. Ada moves closer to me. I see her hands are shaking too. Are we meant to be nervous? Nervous of what? Burying Taata? Speaking to family? I do not understand.

We enter the ugly building, and are greeted by more men, they speak of further things I do not understand, I rock Juliet on my shoulder as we are led through another door, back to the outside. There is a crowd in front of us now, some that I recognise. I see Kasama, and smile and wave, but he does not look at me. His eyes are cold, they stare at a hole in the ground. As we approach, a hush falls, and a tall man calls out. He speaks Taata's name, and some of the women, Mother included, begin to cry. His coffin is carried in. I know Taata is in there. He has been wrapped in bark cloth, the same cloth that has been used to make Mother's dress, one fabric, two uses, a fabric for life and a fabric for death. As the coffin comes closer, Mother's wail becomes louder. In turn others wail louder too. I am forced to whisper 'Shh' to Juliet in the hope she will stay asleep.

The coffin is lowered into the pit, next to where other bodies are buried. There are rows, each marked in their own way. The man speaks some more words and then we are led into another room, most of the people follow us. As they crowd into the small room, I lose sight of the windows and doors and I am instantly uncomfortable. I feel a threat. We are not welcome here.

An elderly man shuffles to the front of the room, flanked by two younger men, both dressed in suits. The man on the left has a large scar down his face, and an eye which looks glazed over. Even under his suit I can see he is very muscular. He glares at Mother, and then at us, his one good eye resting on Juliet as she sleeps in my arms. I do not like the way he stares at her. The room is silent now and the elderly man clears his throat to speak.

'My son has been killed, and we are here to discuss the future of his assets.' I realise he is my step-grandfather. Mother has always referred to him as Bastard whenever Taata was not around. I wonder if we have things in common.

'We have given some thought to how his assets should be distributed in the period since his death, and these are our conclusions.' There are long words being used, complicated terms and I am struggling to keep up.

'The estate is to be returned to his immediate family.' Mother is crying once more, she is speaking to Taata's Father, pleading with him to reconsider, asking him to think of the children. Scar-face turns and whispers something in the old man's ear. He nods.

'Things may have been different should you have birthed a son, but as there is no next of kin what can I do?' He takes a moment and then continues, 'As the baby is his, we can offer you a few more assets should you give me my granddaughter.' His eyes fix on Juliet. 'We can raise her as part of this family, and you may get a bit more money.'

I watch Mother carefully. Is this how I ended up alone in Iris's home? She has traded a child before to help a situation. Will she do it again? I hold Juliet tightly; my chin nestles in her hair.

Mother looks horrified. She raises herself to her full height, and she snatches Juliet from my arms. I am suddenly scared that perhaps she really will hand her over, but no, she turns her back on the crowd, holding her baby tightly, and storms out of the concrete building, back into the sunshine. Scar-face follows us to the door as we race after Mother.

'Where are you going?' He shouts after us.

'Home, we are going home.' Mother calls back, but does not turn to face him, nor to say any final goodbyes to Taata. That chapter of her life is now closed. Ada, Hope and I run to keep up with her. Mother clutches Juliet so tightly that she has woken and is wailing. The clan behind us is no longer interested. Taata's father shakes his head as we flee, but the others have already returned to the ugly innards of the building. I wonder why Mother is still running, there is no one chasing us. Juliet is a girl. They will not fight for her. Mother maintains her furious pace, and as we near home I realise why.

The old man's words resonate around my head, 'the estate is to be returned to his immediate family.' What does this mean? What is Taata's estate? His house? It becomes clear as our home comes into view. Mother cries out as she sees that our belongings have been flung all over the street. Everything we call our own. The doll Hajat gave me is pressed face down in the dirt. My nightdress hangs torn from the branch of a small tree in the front yard, as though it has been thrown from the window. Mother places a screaming Juliet down in the yard on her back, and is desperately trying to gather her personal items, stuffing underwear into her handbag, her back turned away from the prying eyes of neighbours. Ada and Hope silently collect the remaining items. It does not take long. Most of the things in the house belonged to Taata. Mother struggles to stuff all her delicates into her handbag. Suddenly she loses her composure and flings her handbag to the floor. She runs at the front door.

'Why are you doing this to me?' She bangs her fists on the polished wood. Even if she succeeds in crashing it open, then what? We can't just walk back in and carry on living as we were. The door, of course, does not budge. They have padlocked it against us. What was once our home now looks like a small prison. All the laughter and joy in that house is gone. Mother gives up and lies in the dirt alongside her screaming infant. There is little difference between the two of them, both kicking their legs, banging their hands, and drawing unwanted attention. Ada and I stalk the yard, ensuring we have not missed anything. Beside the front door is a pair of weighing scales with a small note tied around the base. I collect the note, but the writing is very loopy. I pass it to Ada. She makes out a handful of words.

'Sell and pay your way back to your village, where you belong.' She reads out loud. Despite her howling, Mother has heard her words and howls even louder. Juliet is now quiet, alarmed by the noise her own Maama is making and unable to compete with it.

'I have nowhere to go, I am not welcomed there, what do I do?' Mother cries harder. A large group of people have gathered on the opposite side of the road. Young boys laugh and point as they jest with each other. I am so embarrassed. Mother needs to pull herself together. If the children can remain so calm, then why can't she? I do not understand the need for so many tears. Mother has cried for days. Crying will not help us. She is lucky, Taata treated her well, she has the means to return to her village. She has not been hurt by Mussa. Things can't be so bad?

'Maama,' I say, and try to help her up. Her eyes sharpen through her tears.

'Do not Maama me,' Her hand swipes and slaps me hard on the cheek, making me fall back in surprise.

Her hand draws back to strike me again, and I cower from her, but she drops her arm, as if all her energy has suddenly drained away. Slowly, she starts to gather more of our things from the dirt, then begins walking down the road, Juliet on her hip, the other two girls trailing behind. I stand and brush the sand from my dress, collect my belongings and begin to follow Mother and my sisters down the street. She may not want me, but I simply have nowhere else to go.

Chapter Eighteen

'Good Morning sleepy head.' I hear a soothing voice drifting into my ear, disturbing my slumber. The voice is soft, calm, and I feel a smile spread across my lips. We are at Beatrice's. On that first evening we walked miles. The smaller children were crying with weariness while Mother tried to decide where to go. She eventually settled on Beatrice's house. Beatrice, her best friend, like Maama, has no man in her life anymore. She was happy to take us in. We have been here two months, and while Beatrice is kind and good, it is very cramped here. Mother sleeps in the same room as us four girls, our bodies pressed together side by side. Even on the coldest nights it is difficult not to sweat. Mother talks in her sleep, she calls for her beloved husband. Hope has taken to calling for him too. Ada and I lie side by side, avoiding the flailing arms and legs from the disturbed sleepers. She sometimes holds my hand, but we do not talk, just wait for sleep to finally catch up with us.

Mother is usually gone by dawn. I do not know where Mother goes when it is so early, but I know it is not my place to ask. Anyway, I am always grateful for my day to begin with Beatrice.

'Come now beautiful girl, time to get up, we must get you fed.' I yawn and stretch as my bleary eyes focus on her smiling face. I am dazed, as I always am these days, through lack of sleep, and she takes my hand and leads me through to the crowded kitchen. The volume is loud in there. Little girls everywhere squabbling over food. The baby crying, Beatrice's own children arguing with Hope. Ada is seated already. From her swollen eyes and weary shoulders, I can tell she has not slept at all. She worries. I can see her worrying now as the children steal food from one another. I may be sleepy, but I too reach out for torn slices of chapatti and fruit as Beatrice places little plates down on the table. I have gone too often without food to miss the chance to grab it whenever I can. Ada eats nothing, so I pocket a sneaky handful, to give her something to nibble on later.

'Are you sick?' I ask her across the table. She shakes her head. I move around the table to be close to her.

'You did not eat?' I pry again.

'Don't you see, there is not enough food.' Her eyes are fixated on the empty plates.

'I know but you could have had something?' I do not yet offer her the tokens I pocketed, as I suspect she would not eat them.

'There is less food today than there was yesterday.' She looks at me now, her eyes sharp, glaring directly into my own.

She is right. I may be young, but I can also see that Beatrice has gone without breakfast. She continues to rally the children ready for school in her usual cheery way, but every now and then she stops to catch her breath, or steady herself against the table. I don't remember if she ate supper last night either. She notices we are watching her.

'Come on ladies, time for school, those clothes won't get on those bodies without a bit of help.' She dismisses us from the table with a smile, but her eyes look worried.

Ada and I return to the tiny bedroom. Hope is already there wrestling with the buttons on her school blouse. Ada pulls me to the corner.

'Lela, this is serious, there is less and less food by the day. Beatrice can't support us all. She works but she doesn't make enough money for all of us.'

'What about Mother? Where does she go every morning, she must be working, no?'

'I don't know.' What could she possibly be working at before the day has even properly begun?

As if on cue we hear the front door swing open as Mother returns, earlier than most days. She exchanges a few words with Beatrice and then she enters the bedroom.

'Don't bother dressing for school.'

'What do you mean, Mother?' Ada asks, panicked. School is her refuge.

'You are doing chores today, leave the uniform.' She returns to the kitchen.

'This is crazy.' Ada is angry. I have never seen her so angry before. Her school skirt is thrown to the floor as she puts the clothes she wore to bed back on, forcing her shirt violently over her head. She pulls on a pair of shoes too, as though she is expecting to leave the house.

'Mother,' she calls as she follows her into the kitchen. 'Mother, we need to talk.' I suddenly see that the child in Ada has now gone. I didn't see her leave, but here instead is a forthright young woman, one plagued by responsibility, and worry for her family.

'What do you say to me, child?' She has adopted her fighting voice, ready to put the girl back in her place.

'There is no food, and now no school? Mother there is no money, we cannot live like this. It's not fair on Beatrice and it's not fair on her family. They haven't eaten properly in days, and neither have we.'

'Ada, it is not your place to speak to me like this.'

'I am not a child anymore. This family is mine as much as yours and I am not going to see us starve to death. We need school too. You have always told us that without school we shall end up in the gutter.'

'And I assume you are going to pay for this education huh? Now you are a big strong woman? What work will you do? Whore yourself on the streets? Pleasure the drunk men as they leave the bars, a pretty girl like you should do well. Better than me, everything tight, nothing spoilt by childbirth.' Both are enraged now, their skin radiating heat. Mother continues, 'Do you not think I am trying? I am trying to make money, I am trying to help Beatrice, I try every day, but I am good for nothing. I am older now, not as agile as the younger women. There are always younger ones to employ over me.'

The fury has not dissipated yet. They stare at each other, their eyes locked.

'What about the weighing scales?' I wonder out loud. 'You were left the weighing scales to sell to return to your village? Is it not time to use them?'

'Stupid girl,' Mother hisses in response. 'Do you suppose I still have them? Do you think they're tucked away in my back pocket for a rainy day? Hidden in my bosom? They were sold on day one. They have kept you fed, clothed and schooled these past months, though, perhaps, the schooling was wasted on you. Iris always said you were an idiot.'

105

Her words sting, but she is not finished.

'Even if I still had them, what is there for me, for us? Unwelcome, called a whore, a prostitute, a liar? Sold to the cheapest bidder perhaps? That is no life.'

'There will be no life here either Mother, if we carry on like we are.' Ada speaks again, although softer now, her ferocity diminished somewhat. 'What life will we have if there is nothing to eat? I am happy to find work. I can help, but whatever I bring in will not support such a large family.'

'No, no.' Mother shakes her head sadly and looks at her feet. Her anger too has abated. 'No, you shall not work girl, but you are right, something does need to change. I have been thinking of it, it has troubled me, Beatrice, to put you and your family through all this. The small dinners this week, the smaller breakfasts, having to take my children out of school, well that's it, it is decided.'

'What is decided Maria?' Beatrice asks, concerned.

'Do not worry yourself, Beatrice. The girls and I shall be moving on shortly. It's almost time.'

'Almost time for what?

'Almost time for a wedding, Beatrice.'

'Oh no Maria, no, not him. We shall sort it out, Maria, a job will come in time.' Beatrice's chin wobbles as she pleads with Mother to reconsider whatever decision she has come to. We do not understand what she means.

'Do not worry, my friend, he is to be my husband and you will be free from this burden. Girls, it is almost time to meet your new Taata.'

Chapter Nineteen

Stood in a line, side by side with my sisters, I am excited at the prospect of meeting my new Taata. Things progressed quickly after Mother first mentioned him. Not another word was said on the subject for a whole fortnight, then suddenly we are here, at his house, dressed in our best clothes, some parts of them torn and old, but we have scrubbed up as best we can, ready to meet him.

We wondered if her silence meant that the whole marriage project had fallen through, but our food situation improved. One day there was a whole basket of fruit waiting for us early one morning, then we had fresh meat delivered to us. Ada said the food must have been offerings from him, buttering us all up so we would accept him. She said Beatrice didn't like him. I wasn't so sure. Why would he need to please us? Mother is still pretty, yes, but she is mean, and not so young these days, plus she has a horde of illegitimate children following her around. If I were a man, I think she would have to send me presents for me to marry her. 'Don't even think of ruining this for me, girl,' she hisses, as if she can read my thoughts. I am hardly the cause of her problems.

I look away from her sour face and smooth down the creases in my dress. As soon as I was told we were leaving Beatrice's to move in with our new Taata, I knew I had to make the best impression possible. In my experience it is the Taatas that bring joy in this world. Ada, on the other hand, lay there for quite some time after the rest of us washed and dressed. When she finally got up, she went to find Beatrice, who was hanging laundry.

'Beatrice?'

'Hello Ada, all ready for your big day?' She seemed just as cheerful as always.

'You do not like him, do you?' Beatrice, not prepared for such bluntness, folded a sheet over her right arm and pursed her lips.

'What makes you say that?'

'You have barely spoken to Mother since she first mentioned him. Did you fight over him?' I had not noticed they hadn't been speaking, but then whenever Mother is in any room I try and make myself scarce, fearful of her spiteful tongue.

'So long as he makes your Mother happy, that's what counts.'

'But does he make Mother happy? Or is she marrying him for his money? Or for convenience?'

'You are a bright one, young Ada, but really it is not my place to answer these questions. If you have concerns, you should voice them with your mother.'

'She would tell me it is not my business, maybe worse.'

'Yes, perhaps, and I am sorry for that.' Beatrice stopped for a moment and looked down at the dusty yard beneath her feet. At last she spoke: 'Girls, I want you to be safe, and happy, that's all. I care for all four of you like you are my children, just like I care for your Mother too. Despite what you think she has your best interests at heart. Now you both must make sure you are ready. The car comes soon. Don't forget your things.' She turned away.

'Our best interests at heart.' I am repeating that sentence in my head, awaiting his arrival. Given Mother's insistence that we all dressed in our best, I was convinced we would be in another fine house, with fancy, smart chairs like our last home. Not so. The house is a short distance from Beatrice's, in the same run-down part of town, where all the houses seem small, and shabby. There is very little furniture, just a simple dusty looking armchair in one corner, and two plastic chairs. On the seat of the armchair there is a battered book which has loopy writing on the cover, and a worn leather spine. It looks as though it is often read. The floor is dusty, much like the furniture, but in the corner of the room there is a long thin rug, which seems cleaner. It reminds me of the rug in Jaaja's kitchen. Much of the plaster on the wall is decayed and the only window has a large crack in it. Behind where we stand there is a curtain draped from a rusty looking pipe, suspended from the ceiling. Through a crack I see a mattress. Ada is sweating beside me, although the room feels quite cool. Perhaps she is sick.

'He is coming girls, please stand straight.' Mother hisses, to no one in particular. All our eyes focus on the door as the handle is turned and the figure of a man enters. He is nothing like the image I have had in my head. His scant hair is grey and wiry. He is short, too, and squat. He is dressed in a simple grey cloth robe, which has holes in places, and patches on the sleeves, over equally tatty trousers. In his hand are a length of wooden beads which he fiddles with as he examines us one by one. Ada is first in the line of girls. Her hands are shaking by her sides. As his face peers at hers I wonder if she might faint, but then he moves closer to me, without saying anything and looks at my features closely. It looks as though he is searching for something. I consider introducing myself but the way he stares is unnerving and my confidence is lost.

Hope, on the other hand does not seem put off and smiles up at her new Father. 'Hello Taata. I am Hope.' She has just lost her first tooth and she wears the gap proudly. Our new 'Taata' does not smile.

'Did I ask you to speak?' he grunts.

'I am sorry, she is still very young.' Mother murmurs from behind him.

'Well, it's clear there has been very little discipline in the past weeks, but you are now in my house and there are rules here to be followed. You shall not speak to me unless I ask you to. I will not have feral children in my home, is that clear?'

Hope does not respond, her eyes flit from his face to Mother's, then she turns to me, her face panicked.

'I said is that clear?' This time his voice louder, and she jumps with fright, managing a small nod in agreement. His voice has made Juliet jump too and she begins to wail and reach for her Mother. Mother, in turn, goes to pick her beloved babe from the floor but the man stops her.

'Leave her, she needs to learn too.' My Mother's face contorts with pain as she is pushed away from her crying infant.

'Sorry looking bunch, aren't they?' he mutters to her as he turns his back to us. Three kind fathers were obviously too much to ask for. I have seen this person before. The need to control. The need to feel superior. The need to humiliate, to bully, to lash out. Iris is back, only this time in the body of a man.

Somewhere in the distance I hear the muezzin calling to the faithful. Taata turns back to face us.

'It is prayer time, on your knees.' We watch as Taata moves the rug to the centre of the room and kneels upon it, his body carefully positioned, 'Do it.' he snaps again. All but Juliet obey, though we do not know what we are doing. Even Mother looks concerned, but she mimics his movements as he bows to some invisible entity. Juliet, who has stopped crying, uses this moment to toddle to her much-wanted Mother, while he watches, clearly irritated. This time he says nothing but mutters a pattern of words to himself between bows. We copy for several minutes until he rises to his feet once more.

'If that child does that ever again during prayer time then I shall give her something to cry about.' He sneers at Mother before storming out of the house, slamming the door behind him.

Once he has left Ada and I glare at Mother, looking for a reaction, for an explanation. She gives nothing away. After a deep breath she clears her throat once more and turns towards the curtain.

'Well, come on now, we can't stand around all day. This is home now. Put your belongings neatly next to the mattress and we shall get on with the cooking.'

Hope is happy to obey; she is always a happy child. She rarely questions, or answers back. I too walk towards the mattress. No good will come of questioning Mother here. Ada, however, stands rooted to the spot, her fists clenched, sweat still pouring from her brow. When Mother sees she has not joined us behind the curtain she turns.

'Well?'

'Well? Is that all you have to say.' Ada speaks through clenched teeth.

'You bring your things and set them down here. Do it *now*.' Mother raises her voice slightly, though not enough to draw attention, I assume in case our new Taata is near.

'You mean to tell us that you left Beatrice's, you took us away, away from where we were safe to *here?*' She moves her head from side to side examining the starkness of the bare room, then continues. 'You want us to live with *that man?* We have been here less than twenty minutes, yet he has already threatened a toddler. She puffs out her chest to imitate him: *'I'll give her something to cry about?'* I would like to give him something to cry about.' Her whole body is trembling now. I have never seen her like this before, pure hatred in her eyes, a rage which will not easily dissipate.

Mother snatches at Ada's ear, pinching it between her fingers. Ada inhales sharply with pain. Mother's teeth are clenched as she hisses in Ada's ear.

'You are a spoilt brat, you know that, spoilt and ungrateful. Well girl, you listen here, this is our home now. We can't afford anywhere else, so you must put up with it. It's here or the streets, so you can drop that attitude, or you can leave. You understand?'

'Oh, I do.' Ada responds. She shows no fear or remorse. She throws her spare clothes hastily into the corner. I see quite clearly that she has every intention to do just that. Leave.

We move into the crowded kitchen area. He is nowhere to be seen. The kitchen itself is not much more than a cupboard, barely enough room for us all to stand while we chop. There is no room for a stove so Ada has the task of building a fire outside, so we may cook the vegetables. We prepare the food in silence. I realise then how lucky I had been, with Taata number two and then at Beatrice's. Mother, yes, was always there, with her sarcastic remarks and ready hand, but there was never the uneasy unknowing. The unknowing that comes from a different type of predator, the sort always looking for a fight. I feel the old sensation, a feeling I had not felt since I had left Iris's. A deep knot in the pit of my stomach, twisting tighter with every distant sound, with every footstep that passes the yard. I had met this new Taata for barely minutes, yet I already know his type. I know what he is capable of. When he returns, no doubt full of alcohol, the question is not if, but when he strikes his first victim, and who will it be?

Chapter Twenty

We ate quietly before he returned. Juliet dozed on Mother's lap. Every now and then Mother stroked the top of Juliet's head, where her hair was still baby soft. I watched her face relax as she glanced wearily down at the sleeping infant. It had been torture for her earlier, not being allowed to pick up her baby. She loved Juliet with the same intensity that she hated me.

We cleared the dishes, Mother glancing into the darkness, awaiting his return. This part of town was busier than Beatrice's. Crowds of men passed, all full of the drink, calling to each other, laughing, even the odd fight, but no sign of him. Then we were ordered to bed.

I find myself once again staring at cracks on yet another wall. Somehow Mother and the girls are all asleep. Even Ada is snoring softly beside me, her hand clenched firmly around mine. I have tried, but I can't doze off. My stomach hurts. I am not sick, except with anxiety. The street outside has grown quieter, the hordes of men have thinned. The bars will be closing soon, and our new Taata will return.

I hear the door bang open. Ada, beside me, jolts awake immediately. Her eyes are round, like saucers, her pupils dilating with shock. I draw my finger sharply to my lips. The worst thing to do now is to betray that we are awake. I take her hand and clasp it firmly in mine, then we close our eyes tightly and attempt to level our panicked breathing. His breathing is hoarse, his body sounds heavy as it knocks against a plastic chair, making it screech on the concrete floor. He throws a shoe to the floor, then throws the other against the wall. Ada's hand tightens around mine even more. Pins and needles prick at my fingertips, and I want to tell her to loosen her grip but I daren't speak.

'Wife.' His deep, guttural voice growls from the living room. 'Do I not have a wife in there?' He is walking clumsily towards the curtain. I open my eyes, suddenly concerned for the babies, closer to that side than we are. I see Mother, her eyes clenched like Ada's. She has drawn the flimsy, moth-eaten bedsheets close to her chest, her body flinches with each of his footsteps. She is awake too.

The curtain is drawn back. The dim light from the living room bright enough to make the little ones stir.

'Stay asleep, please stay asleep,' I mutter to myself repeatedly.

'Well, this looks cosy,' he laughs. 'All these women just for me?' He reeks of the drink. I can smell it from here, rancid breath that makes my stomach turn even more. As his eyes begin to adjust to the darkness, he is examining the row of seemingly peaceful females.

'I could have my pick, eh?' He snorts with laughter, and then belches loudly. I am beginning to think if he were to vomit, right here, it would be the better option. Instead, he sways above the still body of Mother, lying in the middle of her four daughters.

'Come on wife, it's our first night together as a married couple, you know what that means?' He kicks at her legs to turn her body from its side onto her back. She inhales sharply, and a small murmur comes from her throat, almost like a tiny scream. Her eyes are open now, wide, scared like Ada's.

'No!' Mother demands, 'Not here, not in front of my children.' She forces herself to her feet, trying to muscle him out of the way, but she struggles to stand, and he uses brute force to push her down once more.

'I am the man here, this is my house, you will do as you are told.' His right foot presses down on her groin area, preventing her from moving again as he clumsily fiddles with the buckle on his belt. She scratches at his leg, doing her best to fight him off, without waking the babies. Ada, her back to Mother opens her eyes again, unable to believe what she is hearing. I nod, a tiny terrified nod in the darkness, to confirm her worst thoughts are true. She closes her eyes again, her eyelids clamped shut, eyelashes entwined.

He has finally unbuckled his belt and his trousers fall to the floor. As they slip down, I clamp my eyes once more. I lie still, but my breathing will surely give me away. Neither he, nor Mother says another word, but Ada flinches beside me as he rests an arm on her, lowering himself into position.

'No, not here.' Mother begs again, more quietly, but he ignores her pleading. Her voice is suddenly muffled, as though he has covered her face. Then he begins to use her. He grunts through the darkness. I picture the buffalo, in the grasslands, they make the same noise. I try and think of them now.

'My wife, I will have you wherever I want, whenever I want. You are a whore, with your whore children. It's all you are good for.' Like I said before, Iris in a man's body.

Mother is crying now, and screaming, though it is still muffled, but I can hear tiny sobs over his grunts. My heart breaks for her.

'Whore,' He repeats between each grunt, each time his voice getting louder, his movements gather momentum. I am certain it will be over soon; it must be. Please be over, please be over, please be over. As expected, he cries out and as he does so, he slaps her across her face with such intensity I can't help but open my eyes. I see him rise, naked, bar a dirty vest dripping in sweat. He kicks Mother's foot out of his way then stumbles wearily to the living room. We wait in silence until we are serenaded by his snores, once more reminiscent of the buffalo. He is asleep, for now we are safe.

I look for something, anything, to be sick into. My finest dress is the only thing to hand, discarded depressingly alongside me. I hurriedly cup the dress into my hands and retch into it, quickly, but violently into the course fabric. Ada pats my back. Folding the fabric over on itself, to contain the sick, I survey my surroundings. Ada watches me with concern, although she too looks like she may vomit. Mother has once more pulled the bed sheet closer to her body, but she does not hide everything, her breast is showing where he ripped at her nightgown, and I see the tears tattooing her skin. For a second, she looks no older than Hope, lost and afraid in the house of a man who has raped her. Then she remembers herself, she straightens out her torn night gown, then turns her back on Ada and me. Mercifully, Hope and Juliet remain asleep.

The fabric in my hands begins to grow damp and I know I must dispose of the contents. I shiver at the thought of passing him to walk to the latrine, but I have little choice. I silently rise to my feet, delicately stepping around my sisters. I turn before reaching the curtain and wonder if Mother might come with me, but her eyes are firmly shut, though the lines made from tears glinting in the light give her away. Ada is too terrified to move. I turn again towards the living room and peer around the grubby fabric. He is there, snoring, still half naked. His mouth is open. He is sweaty, and his privates are on show. It's enough to make me heave once again. I tiptoe past him as fast as I can and make it to the fresh air outside. In the darkness, alone, I allow myself to heave and gag until I have nothing left to regurgitate. I want to remove all the badness. Erase the sounds I heard tonight, the smells that infiltrated my nostrils. I want it all gone.

I collapse against the wall of the yard and look up at the stars. Once again, I am truly helpless. For years with Iris, I had wished for my own Maama to save me from her and Mussa. How ridiculous. She couldn't save me. She can't even save herself.

Chapter Twenty-One

We rise late. The two younger girls have been up for hours, playing with the few toys they still possess. Mother has been awake for hours too, just staring at the ceiling. Even Juliet and Hope can't rouse her from her hypnotic state. Neither Ada nor I slept. Sometime after returning to bed, just as dawn approached, I heard him stir, muttering to himself, still in a drunken stupor. He crashed around in the small space and for a terrifying moment I thought he may approach the curtain, ready for round two. Instead he coughed and fumbled with a door handle, heading towards the latrine. I lay transfixed, listening for his return, but it's been several hours now, and he has not come back. He is probably passed out there, still on the toilet. I do not wish to be the one to find him there. I can't dismiss the image of him, half naked, slumped in a chair.

The day is getting on. Juliet becomes fidgety. Crying at intervals. She is a good-natured toddler, but even her temper is frayed when hungry. None of us speak to one another but we are all weighing up our options and working out which scenario will have the best outcome. Stay here, but risk a screaming, starving toddler that may enrage him or risk bumping into him, hung over and irritable? Ultimately, we do not have an option. The babies need feeding. Mother barks at me.

'Lela, feed the infants, I need to wash.' I am not entirely surprised that it is me being sent into the firing line. Still, I was hoping we could face the wolf together. Ada grabs my arm, holding me back.

'Do not go, he is out there.' She looks petrified.

'Ada, you go too.'

Ada stares at her Mother, all respect gone. She folds her arms. 'You go. You got us into this mess.'

'What did you say?'

'You heard me. Why send children near that beast, you made your bed, you lie in it.'

'Well then leave, go ahead and starve for all I care. How do you expect me to feed you all without him?'

I am frightened, anxious, and my head aches. I can't face a fight. We should be united.

I take Ada by the hand and hold onto her tightly. Hope and Juliet follow, Juliet toddling brightly, Hope humming to herself. Both oblivious to last night's events.

In the kitchen there is still no sign of him. We set about arranging breakfast, but the pickings are slim. There are scraps of food abandoned on the side, the remnants of some sort of late-night feast. There is some fruit in a bowl, covered with flies, so I take the time to wash each item carefully before cutting it into bite sized pieces. Ada and I leave the leftovers for Mother, neither of us able to face food now. I sip at water gently, still waiting for my stomach to settle.

Hope needs the latrine, so we agree to go as a group. He is sleeping off the drink in the sunshine. The sun is warm, and I am sure he will burn, but I will not be waking him. His mouth is wide open, facing the sky, attracting more insects with his wretched breath.

'What's he doing?' Hope enquires.

He has at least managed to dress himself.

Ada and I keep the younger girls quiet, each of us taking turns to hurry on the latrine while the others keep watch, eyes firmly fixed on him as though he is a sleeping lion.

As we re-enter the house, we hear him stir. He coughs, then heaves as though vomiting the last of the alcohol. Then comes a hideous noise of throat clearing and spitting. Hope pulls a face in humorous disgust. Ada and I are desperate to get ourselves and the little ones away from him.

'Quick, hide.' We shuffle the girls along a narrow passageway and search desperately for somewhere to hide the younger two. The starkness of the property becomes even more apparent. There is nothing here, no tiny cupboards, no hidden rooms. Ada is panicking, I see the beads of sweat once more, the protective instinct of the eldest showing through. He is still spitting and throat clearing as he enters the kitchen to investigate the food situation. He swears as he finds there is less there this morning than he found last night. We reach the area behind the curtain. Mother glances at us absently. She is dressed but curled on her mattress clutching her stomach. She looks as though she is in pain. She does not recognise our panic, or perhaps she doesn't care. Ada spies a small barred window high, near the ceiling.

'We won't fit through there.' I read her mind.

'We won't, but they will.' She nods at Hope beside me and Juliet in my arms. My throat catches. What if they get hurt in the fall on the other side? But it is far more dangerous for them to stay in here. We grab an armful of sheets and launch them through the bars to cushion the fall. Ada then boosts me high enough to feed the girls gently through the gap. Hope is first, she is a heavy little lump, and complains as she does not feel our fear.

'You're hurting me, stop it Lela.' But she is through and listens to instructions to catch Juliet and hide in the corner between the wall and a shrub. Grumbling, she does as she is told. As Ada and I move away from the window, he pulls the curtain wide open.

He curls his lip.

'You got rid of the brats. Good.' He doesn't speak to Mother, and doesn't acknowledge her obvious discomfort, but shoves her to one side, making room for himself on the mattress.

'Fetch me milk.' He orders Ada, throwing a handful of pennies at her feet.

'Why should I?' She snaps. My head darts sharply to look at her. Why is she antagonizing the beast?

'Because I tell you to, girl, do it.'

'No.'

Mother sits up straight.

'You respect your elders, girl. Do what your Taata says.'

'That pig is not my Taata, he can fetch his own milk.' Ada spits, and throws the change back in his face. He is quickly enraged, pulling himself to his feet with a speed I would not expect from a heavily hungover, ageing man. He grabs Ada around her throat and pins her to a wall. Her hands scratch at the skin on his arms, she cannot breathe.

'Let go,' I shriek, 'you are hurting her, let go.' I grab his arm and try to pull it away from her. He stares into her eyes with a ferocious anger.

'Drop her, drop my daughter!' Mother screams, struggling to rise from the mattress, clutching at her stomach.

119

'Shut up, or you and your whore children can go back to the streets and starve!'

It's only when Ada herself starts to choke that he gets bored and drops her to the ground. I fall to my knees and hold my sister close, she gasps for breath, clutching me with one hand and rubbing at her neck with the other. She finds the strength to rise to her feet. He glances casually at her.

'Go get that milk now.'

She pauses for a moment, taking two or three deep breaths then speaks.

'I said no.' Her hoarse voice manages, he looks up in surprise, clearly not expecting further insolence.

'Get out of my house.'

'I envy the people who haven't met you,' Ada spits then turns to Mother, 'I am leaving, I will be at Beatrice's if you want me.' She squeezes my hand one more time, then glances at me apologetically before leaving. I look at her back in dismay. I long to scream at her, how can you leave me here? How can you abandon us? Please don't leave me alone with him, with Mother, the only one to defend the little ones. Please help me. She does not turn back, and in all honesty, I wish I could be as brave as her. I wish I could walk out too. I want to leave them, leave them all behind, make my own way, but where would I go? I have walked out once before, but that was with the certainty that my Mother was out there somewhere, waiting for me. There is no one out there for me now. I have nobody. As I turn my eyes back towards Mother and my so called new Taata I see him studying me, as though he is reading my mind.

'Don't you get any ideas girl; you are staying here.' He grabs my shoulders and pushes me hard against the wall. For such an unfit individual, he is incredibly strong. My struggles are useless.

'Mother, Mother help me, help me.' I plead, but she rolls onto her side, so she can no longer see me.

'Please don't, sir, I will get your milk, please don't hurt me.' His eyes investigate mine.

'Go and get it,' he sneers. 'And don't get any ideas from your sister, or you will not survive, understand?' He lets go of me and I fall to the floor, gasping and unable to speak. I collect the small change, nod in his direction and escape, be it for just a minute to fetch milk. I am not bothered now at how unsafe this neighbourhood may be. There is nothing, bar killing me, that can come close to this hell that I am living in.

Chapter Twenty-Two

I am forced to refer to him as Taata. The man is a monster. I'm in a constant state of exhaustion, as I am truly living in a war zone. My old life with Iris and Mussa was horrific, but now I witness it happening to Mother. It has been months now, watching Mother raped, cut and beaten by him. She fights, she fights with everything she has, like I did, but he is strong.

Ada pops her head in when she is certain he is out. She works now; cleaning, running errands, but enough to pay for a little extra food. I long to do the same, but I can't leave the younger two. He hits them often. Hope gets slapped daily; her playful spirit extinguished. She cringes and flinches when she hears his voice. Even Juliet is not safe. He likes to hit and strangle me, often just because he feels like it. Mother, never able to stop him.

Occasionally I escape. My stepfather has a fondness for milk, often late at night, or if he is particularly hung over it is the only thing he wants to drink. I am always the one sent out on the milk missions. Anything to escape our tiny hole of hell. Late at night however, the task is not so simple. The streets are full of drunk men who try to grab me or simply yell hideous things at me. I try to be quick, but that late it is not always easy to find milk, and I dread coming home empty-handed. Today however, the sun is shining, and I am grateful to be outside. It has been weeks since I was sent out. He has had us observing something called Ramadan. I do not know what it is, but Mother, Hope and I have been allowed to eat nothing in daylight hours. Food is scarce anyhow, but to be allowed nothing all day and only the scraps of what he leaves behind at night has meant our stomachs ache with hunger. We then had to spend much of this week at a big building which he refers to as the Mosque. We have had to wear our best clothes. My dress is still indelibly stained with vomit. We spent hours there, but I could understand very little of why we were there or what we were doing. Ramadan has ended now, as we can eat once again, and I have been sent for milk during the day.

I am almost at the shop when I see a group of children gathering in the local square. Adults look on too, each straining their neck to see over the crowd. My curiosity draws me nearer, though I am cautious. In this part of town, crowds are drawn to bad things; fights, murders, beheadings and other horrors. My mind inevitably flits to the burning of the thief. The crowd is listening to someone with a loud, but calm, voice. I crawl under the legs of the throng to get closer. A tall man is standing on an old crate in the centre of the square. He is a very striking man, wearing a beautiful white suit. I have not seen such beautiful clothing before. Around his neck he wears a pretty fabric, full of bright colours, tied in a bow, and in his suit, there is a piece of material which matches, sticking out of his jacket pocket. I can't help but stare. He speaks kindly to those around him, every now and then I see him bend to speak to someone or stroke the head of a child. I don't hear him exactly, but every so often he points into a building behind him. He calls it a church and he says that he has come to help us all be saved. Some follow him inside. I turn my back to continue my quest for milk. I am late, and my stepfather will be outraged. The man makes one last attempt to draw more people in.

'Of course, there will be biscuits at the end, do join us, you are all welcome.'

The word 'biscuits' stands out above all others, like a siren call. I turn on my heels and follow the others into church. As I pass the man in the white suit, he smiles at me.

'Welcome, my child.' His strong hand gently strokes the top of my head. I smile at him, unused to gentle words and gentler touches. The other children are equally as enticed by food, and we are herded towards a small font of water balanced on a child-sized pillar. Another man and a woman are standing near the font and direct the children to sit on the floor near their feet. The adults, few in comparison, seat themselves on a variety of chairs behind us. The man eventually makes his way to the front.

'Welcome, my children, to the house of God, thank you for stepping inside. I am here to tell you about the mission I am on, to save you, to help Jesus Christ enter your life, to save you all.'

He talks about someone called God and someone else called Christ. I have no clue who these people are, but I like the sound of them. He says that they can help with my pain, with my suffering. I have suffered a great deal; my family suffers a great deal too. When I think of them, I never see happiness anymore. I see burdens, I see pain, I have watched my Mother, beaten, raped, hurt. Her stomach is swollen now and I recognise the signs. Another person coming into our tiny house of despair. Perhaps this Jesus can take us somewhere new?

Once he has finished speaking, we line up and receive two biscuit each. This is a treat I have never experienced before. I pocket them quickly, frightened that I may have to share them.

'Thank you, sir,' I say, my voice full of admiration.

'You are very welcome child, but please, call me Father Silver, I am a friend, not a sir.'

'Oh, thank you, Father Silver.'

The church has almost emptied now so instead of leaving with the others, I hide myself towards the back and start nibbling at the biscuits. I have not had anything so delicious since Jaaja fed me treats behind Auntie Iris's house. Father Silver has promised more tomorrow. I will be back, no matter how badly beaten I am this evening. Once the biscuits are finished, I hurriedly make my exit and fetch the milk before returning home. I stare at the front door from afar, loathed to go inside. In resentment I pull the cap off the milk and down half the bottle, refilling the bottle with water from a jerry can propped by the front door, I bet he is too drunk to notice the difference. I enter and see him passed out on the mattress, snoring loudly, Mother grabs me by the arm and whispers sharply.

'Where have you been? He will kill you when he wakes.'

'Good, he will be doing me a favour.'

'Where were you?'

'I went to church.' I offer truthfully, awaiting her response.

'Church?' She draws back, surprised, 'What do you know of church?'

'The men said that Jesus would help us, that he could save us from our struggles.'

She laughs. 'He's welcome to try. You are too old to believe in fairy tales.' She lets go of my arm and breathes loudly, her lips pursed, her hand rests on her lower back. She is more tired these days and does not have the enthusiasm to argue with me any longer. She walks into the yard and starts pacing up and down in the sand, her face turned up towards the sun, contorted. I am not sure if it is pain that alters her appearance, or exhaustion. She has not spoken much of her pregnancy. We can all obviously see her body changing, but she never announced another baby was on the way. I heard him complaining about another mouth to feed. I expect Mother sees it as a burden too, much like the burden I was to her.

I develop a routine, sneaking out to church every day after lunch. Father Silver greets me each time, welcoming me with warm, kind words. I enjoy what he says, but most of all I enjoy the biscuits. It is the last day of the 'Christian crusade', as it is called, and I am lining up for my last round of treats. I have a sad feeling in the pit of my stomach, knowing that my little adventure here is over. It has been a little bit of light in the dimness. 'Taata' drinks more these days and Mother is too tired with the baby coming so I have got away lightly.

As I near the front of the line, Father Silver say, 'Let the little children come to me, for the kingdom of God belongs to them. Let faith, like that of a child, redeem you. For God so loved the world that he gave us his only beloved son. Whoever believes in him will not die but shall have eternal life.'

I think of these beautiful words as I devour the biscuits, melting flaky pastry one last time, that they have spoken much of God and even more of Jesus, but I have seen nothing of this wonderful-sounding pair. I am still hoping Jesus will come and take me away from this life. As the crowd slowly departs, I approach Father Silver.

'Will Jesus come soon? To take me away? To fix my problems?'

Father Silver stares blankly at me for a few moments. I wonder if I have asked an inappropriate question, but then he smiles warmly once more and bends down towards me.

'What is your name, child?'

'Lela.'

'You have come here every day, haven't you?'

'Yes.'

'Why do you like coming here so much?'

'I like the biscuits.' I reply honestly.

He laughs. I like talking to him and do not want him to leave straight away.

'I like the things you say too. I like that you say Jesus can take my troubles away.'

'Listen,' He moves his face closer to mine. 'Do you think your mother or father would allow you to come back on Sunday? We have finished here for now, but on Sunday we have a bus taking families to the big church on the other side of town. We run a Sunday school there.'

'Ooh yes, I'd love that.' I feel myself grinning. Of course, I hope there will be more food, but I revel at the idea of school. I haven't been to school for an age. Mother can't afford the school fees.

'I don't have any money.' I frown, suddenly realising the implication this may have.

'You don't need any. Come here for ten on Sunday morning and you can come with me. We will go and speak to Jesus together.'

I run home from church. The quicker I get home the quicker Sunday will come, then I will meet Jesus himself. Maybe Sunday will be the last day in this pit of hell.

The house is a hive of activity. I see Beatrice and Ada and I break into a sprint. Hope is waiting for me, she is sitting on the wall to the front of the property, her skinny legs dangling over the edge, her frail ankles jigging up and down.

'Lela, where have you been?'

'What is happening? Is everything ok?'

'Lela,' Beatrice waves at me, 'come and meet your sister!'

'The baby arrived.' Hope laughs. 'Another girl!'

I step gently into the crowded room. Mother is lying on the mattress, propped up with our bags and piles of clothes.

She has a bundle in her arms and, as I step forwards, I see movement. A tiny arm thrashes about followed by a tiny cry. Taata leans against the wall. He stares at the baby. I study his face wondering if he will be happier with his own child. If he will be kind to her. I remember the old Taata with Juliet. The look of pride in his eyes, the way he would grin as he spun her around. My stepfather doesn't look pleased. I do not see any pride, any laughter. I do not think he has even touched her yet.

'Another girl,' he says in disgust, and barges his way through the women. Mother's eyes follow him out of the room. She looks sad. Beatrice sees it too.

'So, do you have a name for her?' Beatrice asks, trying to lighten the mood.

'Yes,' Mother smiles again as she looks down at the tiny person, no longer crying, her tiny fist wrapped around Mother's finger. 'This is Elizabeth.'

Chapter Twenty-Three

Elizabeth's birth has been a blessing. No, our 'Taata' has not suddenly changed into a law-abiding, gentle, fatherly type. He is, perhaps, even worse than before, drinking more, staying out later, but his determination to stay away has given us time to simply be, to sit and coo at the baby, to help Mother recover. Because he's out so much, Ada can drop round more than usual. Mother's weariness means she is less vile. With Ada visiting, I have been able to sneak out to Sunday School. I told Ada about it, though I kept my plan to run away with Jesus to myself.

'You know he does not believe in Church; he will beat you, even more than usual. You know how he feels about being a Muslim.'

'Some Muslim he is. If he were a true Muslim, he would not drink or beat little children, or abuse his wife,' I say scornfully. She agrees but is worried for me. I lower my voice and pull her to one side, 'I have been told, Ada, that there is a man called Jesus and he will come and take away our pain, that he will take us to the Kingdom of Heaven. We can all go, there is room for all of us, far away from the Lout.' This is our special name for our 'Taata.' 'There is no suffering in the Kingdom, only love.'

Ada looked at me doubtfully, 'Lela, people who are desperate will believe in anything. Don't get drawn into something if you can't be sure it's true.'

'Ada, I can't give this up. Not if there is a chance, even if it's tiny, to get away from him. Besides, they serve good biscuits.'

She laughs. 'Go if you must. I'll cover for you. I think you really need this church.' So here I am running for the bus. A small crowd has gathered to catch it. It is rickety and looks full and I'm afraid I'll be told there is no room, or that I must pay, but as I stand nervously, waiting for permission to get on, Father Silver calls from the front.

'Jump on board, Lela. I saved you a seat.'

'Father Silver.' I throw my arms around him and he looks slightly taken aback, but then smiles and signals to the driver to start moving.

Spirits on the bus are high, it feels like a celebration. Everyone is smiling. Women at the back are singing and the children join in, waving their hands. I do not know the song but listen intently and sway along in time with the singing, clapping my hands when everyone else does. I soon learn the words. We sing of Jesus. We are praising him, and God in heaven. I think they must be very special to have so many songs written about them. I wonder if I will be taken to heaven today. Perhaps I should have brought my things? Mother would have noticed. Anyhow, I reassure myself. My rags would look terribly out of place. I feel sure that Jesus will have plenty of clothes for everyone.

At last we arrive at church and the party atmosphere continues. For the first time in my life I feel truly welcome somewhere. No one looks down at me, no one asks why I am here, they instead welcome me, and a nice lady hugs me and praises God for my beautiful face. I get a strange warm feeling inside my stomach and I wonder if this is happiness.

The adults remain in the main church room, while I am led with the other children through double doors at the back to a warm and comfortable recess. There is a circle of chairs in the middle and a kind lady instructs us to sit down. I hover at the back as the others find themselves somewhere to sit. The lady sees me hesitating.

'Hello sweetheart, are you Lela? Father Silver told me you were coming. Here, let's find you a chair.' No one tells me that I must sit on the floor. I choose a seat next to a girl, a little younger than me. She has her hair in pretty bunches with a white ribbon tied around each. Her dress is pure white too. I stare at it in the same way I stared at Father Silver's white suit the first time I saw it. Everything is so dusty here in Uganda, how can anyone keep anything so clean? Perhaps heaven is white too. The little girl notices and she smiles.

'It's pretty isn't it? My Taata bought it for me. It is my special Sunday school dress.' I smile at her. For a moment emotion overwhelms me, and I feel a huge loss for my first kind Taata, and the second. I feel tears pricking at my eyes and will them to go away, embarrassed that the little girl may see them, but she has turned away as the lady begins to talk about a place called the 'Ark.'

I love Sunday School. I do not feel uneducated, as I often do in school. Someone called Noah took a load of animals on his Ark, and we get to draw our favourites. I do not really understand the story. I do not know why God would make a flood if he is supposed to be so nice, but I find the morning exciting and we are allowed biscuits and milk at the end of class. I drink my milk greedily. We are never allowed milk at home, as the Lout guzzles it all. As the grown-ups finish their service they come and collect their children from the Sunday school. I wait, looking around expectantly, eyes wide. Of course, I know my parents won't be there.

'Is your Maama here, Lela?' The Sunday school teacher bends closer to my face, as I scan the crowd.

'No.'

'Who do you look for?'

'For Jesus, of course,' I beam at her.

'Oh child, come with me.'

She takes my hand and leads me back to Father Silver, and whispers something to him. He looks at me sadly.

'Lela, do you have troubles at home?'

I shrug my shoulders but do not reply. I had not expected questions. I hadn't prepared answers. If I told them the truth it may get back to 'Taata' and I would be in trouble, but if I don't tell them maybe Jesus wouldn't come for me? I suppose he needs to know my troubles to take me away from them.

'Listen,' Father Silver continues. 'Jesus comes for us all, one day, just so long as we accept him as our lord and saviour. You must believe in him, Lela, truly believe, and pray to him. He will listen for your prayers and will help you with your troubles. Here, take this.' He beings rummaging in a small black bag and pulls out a very small book. It reminds me a little of the book Taata looks at when he prays, but he does not pray to Jesus.

'Take this book. It's called a bible. It can help answer your questions. There are stories about God and Jesus and how they help people. It can help you understand. Look after this book. Read it when you can and come here every Sunday on the bus. You are always welcome here.'

131

I hug him and thank him. It feels good to have someone to trust in once more. I do not know anyone here, but they have all made me feel a part of something and for this I am grateful.

I have been attending church for a few weeks. Somehow, I have got away with it, and have suffered relatively few beatings. Mother has been preoccupied with Elizabeth, and 'Taata' stays out so late on Saturday nights that he is usually still asleep when I get home. Church has made life bearable. I keep my troubles to myself, though I'm sure they know what is going on. They have seen Mother in town with a split lip and bruises on her face just because Elizabeth had kept him awake. I dare not tell. They don't ask any more. Despite my silence I am always welcome.

This morning I am awake earlier than ever. I have been invited to a special service at church, as one of the adults is to be baptised. This means truly accepting God and I hope one day I will be baptised too. There will be a party afterwards. I know sneaking out with my best clothes on will be difficult, so I try and draw attention away from myself. I take Elizabeth from Mother, so she can rest. Elizabeth is sleepy, so I tie her to my back as I prepare breakfast and sweep the yard. When the sun is beginning to heat up, I know it is my time to escape. Elizabeth has woken and is searching my chest for milk. It's a good excuse for waking Mother. While she's preoccupied with the feed, I make my escape, hiding my dress under my clothes. I quietly enter the latrine to remove my messy clothes, hiding them behind a bush, then run to make the bus.

The party is the best thing I have ever seen. After our usual Sunday school meeting, we gather back in the main church. Father Silver directs the children to move the chairs to one side, so we can gather around a large font of water. We all crowd together, buzzing with excitement. I do not hear everything Father Silver says but the man agrees to everything, then Father Silver pushes him under the water. When he emerges, eyes blinking, he has a huge grin on his face, and everyone cheers. Time to party. I have heard about

132

parties, but nothing compared to this. Every adult has bought a meal. Not a simple meal of rice and bread, but a feast, and there are hundreds of grown-ups. Food spreads over every surface. I see meat, rice, salad, fruit, vegetables, at least six different types of posho. I am fed regularly enough these days, but never very much. I had no idea how hungry I was until I see this colossal mound of food. I'm not sure what I'm supposed to do, whether I should hand out the food, what I can and can't eat, but I realise that everyone is tucking in, and we are all welcome to anything. A young lady hands me plates and napkins, spoons and urges me to help myself. Huge dishes are held under my nose. I take spoonfuls of anything I can get my hands on. My plate piles embarrassingly higher, but the grown-ups simply smile and tell me to enjoy. I hide away at the back of the room and stuff each mouthful in like a half-starved warthog, expecting to have it snatched away from me. One plateful down, however, and they are still asking me if I would like more. I can't resist, although my shrunken stomach is beginning to suffer. Instead of eating quite so hungrily, I take a mouthful and then stuff some food into a napkin. My mother and sisters deserve some too.

By the time the party has come to an end I have managed to squirrel away an entire meal for my family over my body. I run home from the bus excitedly. It is rare that I can offer something to them. I picture Mother smiling at me for a change, giving her venomous tongue a much-needed rest. I burst through the front door convinced, as it is late on Sunday, that he will still be out, or sleeping, he is not.

'Where have you been?' Mother grabs me as soon as I walk in.

'Mother, I have bought food.' I begin routing around in my pockets, offering her pieces of chicken, chapati, fruit.

'Did you steal this?' Mother's face is fierce, her question direct.

'No, no I got it from a party.'

'Ha, who would invite you to a party?'

'It was a church party, Mother. A baptism.'

Mother lowers her voice and hurriedly glances behind her. 'Church? I told you. He will kill you if he finds out.'

"I brought you food, Mother.' I thought she'd be pleased. It's hardly in plentiful supply.

She snatches the food from me, then holds me towards my stepfather.

'She has been to church.' I am shocked she would throw me into the lion's den so casually.

He snorts. He is not particularly bothered. Surely if he was a true Muslim he would be? Mother backs away and rocks the tiny sleeping Elizabeth, tucked close to her bosom. He comes closer. I can feel his rancid breath on my neck. I screw my eyes shut, but nothing happens. Slowly, I dare to open one eye.

'So. Church, huh?'

'Y-yes.' I answer weakly then screw up my eyes once more, waiting for his hands to encircle my neck. Strangling me is his favourite punishment.

'And they give you food there?'

'Umm, they did today.' He riffles through the napkins and starts to devour the chicken. He wolfs down the tender meat, savouring the perfectly balanced spices, then he shoots his eyes back at me. He throws the stripped chicken bone to the floor and his hands shoot up around my neck like a vice. He pins me to the wall. My eyes bulge in my head, and my hands weakly scratch at his skin. He looks possessed, manic.

'Stop hurting my children!' Mother slaps at his head, Elizabeth still clutched in one arm, he ignores her.

'Go back to your church and tell them that you are no longer welcome back here empty handed. Come back with food for your family, or you are no longer of use to us.' He drops me, bored once more.

I gather myself. I am used to being strangled. I glare at him, so fed up of being used. Why do I need to have a 'purpose' to be part of the family? I already do far more than my fair share. I snatch my thin cardigan, which gives scant warmth for this time of year. I leave without a word, uncertain if I am able to return. I walk towards the makeshift church in the square, near the bus stop. I do not know if they will still be there or what I will say if they are.

The lights reassure me. The crowds have gone but Father Silver and the Sunday school lady are still there, laughing as they stack chairs into tall piles, still merry from the party. Father Silver hears the creak of the door. He sees me and takes in my bloodshot eyes. It happens every time he strangles me.

'Lela, my child. Come in. Are you ok?'

I enter slowly and remain silent. The teacher lady takes my hand and leads me into the warm room.

'You're so chilly,' she says, and she rubs her hands up and down my arms to warm me while Father Silver wraps me in his suit jacket. They do not press me. They wait until I am settled, until I'm ready to talk. The lady gives me a mug of creamy warm milk. They have always urged me never to lie, so I blurt out the truth. 'My Family do not want me.' I surprise myself at how easily the words flow from my lips, as though facing up to it is entirely natural, something I have always known. Father Silver and my teacher exchange a look. I wonder if they are in love. Love. I wonder what that feels like.

'Tell me what happened, Lela.' She asks softly.

I consider telling them that my eyes are red because I have been strangled, that every day he brings me to the brink of death, just because he likes exerting power, inflicting pain. I am afraid they would not believe me.

'They will not have me at home until I bring food.' This, at least, is believable. And true.

'They could come to church, if they are hungry. We can help them too.' I shake my head.

'My stepfather is Muslim; he does not accept God.'

'Are your family very hungry, Lela?'

I bow my head, ashamed, then nod slightly. "We eat a little every day. They try, but there is not enough for us all. The babies are so thin.' I think of Hope, cowering in a corner, her spirit well and truly vanquished. Her ribs protruding from her skin, her arms long, skinny.

Father Silver picks up a basket. He fills it with the leftovers which are wrapped in shiny paper. He adds bowlfuls, platefuls, more food than my family sees in a month. I wonder if Father Silver was hoping to take it home, but he shows no sign of regret.

'We will take them food, Lela. Show me where you live.'

135

He takes me by the hand, and I lead him home. I hesitate often, afraid of the forthcoming confrontation, but he tugs me gently forward in encouragement. At last we reach the house.

My hand is shaking as I knock gently on the door.

'Who is it?' my stepfather barks.

'It's me, Lela,' I call back weakly.

'We told you not to come back.' His voice is sharp. One of the little ones wails in the background and he hisses at them to be quiet.

'I am with her,' Father Silver speaks, his voice deep, clear.

The door opens a crack. His piggy eyes peer out at us. Mother is behind him.

'What you want?' I am embarrassed at his rudeness.

'I have brought food, as you asked.' My stepfather sees the basket then looks back at Father Silver. 'There will be more, every Sunday, if Lela can come to church. She will return each week with more.' I stare at Father Silver, with gratitude, with pride. He continues to stare at Taata as if seeing all the badness inside him. Taata nods and drops his grip on the door. He grabs the basket and pulls me roughly inside. I am shocked Father Silver does not receive a thanks.

'We will see you on Sunday, Lela. Goodbye.' The door slams shut in his face before I can thank him myself.

The Lout throws me aside and begins tearing at the food, I glare at him angrily, appalled at the ungratefulness.

'It's no wonder God won't speak to you, I wouldn't either if I could get away with it.'

Still with chicken in his teeth he goes once for me once more, but Mother intervenes, punching him across his jawbone.

'She has done what you have demanded, now leave my little girl alone.' He retreats in shock, clutching his face, dazed by the force of the punch. As he recovers, he picks up the plate he feasted from, turns to us and sneers, 'You are all whores,' then walks out the door.

My heart sings, she cares for me after all. I nod gratefully as she tucks into her food, knowing she doesn't fully appreciate how much her gesture means to me.

We have four wonderful days of freedom before he returns.

Chapter Twenty-Four

The church stuck to their promise. They didn't owe us
anything. Taata showing no gratitude whatsoever. Every
week I thanked Father Silver profusely, the other kind people
at Church too. From my so-called parents all they received
was a grab and a slam. Someone different prepared food for
us each week. A charitable Mother making an extra bowlful
on a Saturday evening, one of the elderly helpers, some of the
missionary workers. Whoever it was never said anything. It
was never rubbed in my face. I was never asked for favours in
return, or payment. No one questioned me.

None of the other children ever teased me for being a
charity case, either. Whenever one of the younger children
asked, 'Why is Lela taking that dish home again?' they were
answered tactfully, kindly, not by cruel words or jibes behind
my back. Once I heard that the dish was being taken to my
sick Mother, that I was a kind and loving daughter for
looking after my family so well. I picked up my dish that day
and walked away, the world misty behind tears of happiness.
To be described as a kind and loving daughter was everything
I had ever dreamed of. Of course, it would have been nice if
it had been my own Mother who had said it. I wondered
what they meant by 'sick.' Sick because she is worn out after
the birth of her baby? Sick in the head for marrying the Lout?
What kind of woman marries a man who abuses and strangles
her child?

His lack of gratitude is astonishing. Much to my
annoyance, he stopped going out on Sunday evenings, just so
he can get first go at the food. He claims to be against the
church. He tells me often that I have been led astray by devil
people. That I was just a child and what could I possibly
know about religion. Yet he would wait by the door and
grab the dish from me before I was even through it. Then he
would squat on the bare floor and stuff his face while my
sisters looked on hungrily. Luckily for us the people at church
were more than generous, so there was always food left once
he had finished. Then Mother would eat, and only then
could my sisters and I pick through the remnants. We never
ate together like a normal family. I had hoped on the first

Sunday that Mother and Taata would see just how good the church was. That they had kept their promise, no questions asked. Sometimes I daydreamed that Mother and Taata would say how kind Father Silver was. They would remark that the church was not evil. Mother would like the sound of Jesus helping her, of taking her away from her troubles. We would all start going to church together, the little ones in beautiful fancy dresses. Taata may even be given a job by one of the richer church men. He would earn more money and we would stop being hungry. Taata would repent his sins. He would take me by the hand and plead my forgiveness, in abject sorrow for being such a sadistic pig. I would no longer be afraid of him. Then I would know that Jesus had saved us.

I know my daydreams are ridiculous. All those nights in Iris's house dreaming of my Mother, they had been wishes. Now I have no illusions. I enjoy the fantasy, but I see it for what it is. This family is sick. The very fact that Mother and Taata couldn't say a simple thank you for the food I brought told me that.

The Sunday school food filled me up one night a week, but it was not enough to see me put on weight. I remained skin and bone as always, but I had more energy to play, and I managed my chores without the need to sit afterwards. Hope and Juliet began playing together again. When Taata wasn't around they would sit in the shade of the yard and talk to the ants, making little palaces out of the dust. Sometimes they seemed happy, and this made me feel happy, even if just for a moment.

Mother looked gaunt. I assumed the fatigue was normal with having to breastfeed an infant so often, but she had lost all passion for life. She gradually grew wearier, less feisty, less enthusiastic. I couldn't blame her really. When I first found her, her beautiful Juliet in her arms, the man of her dreams by her side she looked so well. She had married 'Taata' for nothing, for a few scraps of food, for a roof over her children's head. She was half-starved, beaten, raped, and abused, and she received no help with the baby from him, only from me and Ada. A meal once a week is not enough for a breastfeeding woman. However, her spiteful tongue maintained all its vigour, showing no signs of flagging.

It is Sunday again, and today's feast is heavier than usual. The carrier bag weighs down my right arm and cuts into my fingers. It is a load I do not mind carrying. As always, each dish has been carefully sealed and covered with various lids and foils. I haven't yet seen the delicacies that await us, but I can smell them. Even over the rancid smell of the littered street, stinking latrines with their doors open in the heat, raw sewage running freely, the spices hit my nostrils. I am almost home and my stomach rumbles with anticipation, despite the huge lunch I had at church earlier. The street is busy with people, those who are Muslim and have visited the mosques for evening prayer are now returning, and the churchgoers are coming home too. With no work or school, the children play happily in the streets, kicking balls, chasing each other. If I were not carrying my precious cargo, I would be tempted to join in. Ada is standing outside our house with a woman. She looks familiar. I am curious, and I can't lie: I am disappointed at the prospect of sharing our meal with two extra people. I scold myself. Ada would share everything she had with me if she could. Ada hugs me. The woman seems awkward, not looking me in the eye. I wrack my brain as to where I have seen her face before.

'Lela, this is an old friend of Mother's, she found me at Beatrice's.' She does not tell me her name. Ada and the woman are very ill at ease, and I suddenly fear trouble. The bag is heavy, I am hungry, and can no longer wait to figure out what her business is. I open the door and call to Mother.

'Mother, Ada is here with a lady.' Mother is feeding Elizabeth on the mattress, her back propped up against the concrete wall. The wall offers some cooling reprieve in the heat, as the small windows do not offer much ventilation, and the room is thick with body odour. Mother's forehead is beaded with sweat.

Mother slowly prizes Elizabeth from her nipple. The baby's eyes are closed in a sort of milk coma. She darts her head from left to right searching for the absent breast but is too tired to cause a fuss. She rests her head again in defeat and Mother gently places her on the mattress beside Juliet, asleep in nothing but a cloth nappy. Hope runs to me when she sees the food and she follows me into the kitchen area to help serve up. I whisper to her to wait a moment, still guiltily hoping the woman, at least, will leave before we have to share it. Thankfully, my stepfather has not yet returned from evening prayer, or the bar, whatever has taken his fancy. Maybe we will have time to eat before he returns. Secretly, I hope he is at the bar. Though he pretends to be a strict Muslim he is often tempted by the lure of alcohol. His drunkenness is terrible for us, but at least it keeps him away.

Mother recognises the stranger instantly.

She gets up and offers our visitor a drink. Mother remembers her manners, though she does not introduce the lady to us. Ada has joined us in the kitchen area as the woman refuses a beverage. Mother offers her the moth-eaten chair in the front room. We peek at her from around the corner. She is scanning her surroundings, scarcely touching the seat she has been offered, eying it up as though it is filthy, which in fairness, it is. She looks at Mother, standing over her, hands on her hips, then, to our collective astonishment, she bursts into tears.

'I'm sorry, so sorry.' She sobs, her hands cover her face, but she shakes her head from side to side. Mother drops her hands, abandoning the stern exterior.

'What's wrong? Is Kasama ok?'

Kasama. The friend of my second kind Taata, who had been with him when he died. She is Kasama's wife. We are so intrigued that we have forgotten about dinner.

'Kasama is dead.' She cries harder, her hands now removed from her face to search her body for a rag to wipe her tears. Mother finds one for her.

'I am so sorry,' she offers stiffly.

'It is all his fault.' She sobs and replaces her hands over her face, and sinks into the chair, filth or no filth. Mother says nothing. I am bursting with questions.

'Maria, he killed himself.'

I gasp in shock. Mother opens her mouth but Kasama's wife continues to speak.

'He killed himself because of what he did. Oh Maria, he killed your beautiful husband. He loved you so much. He was so kind, so good to all your girls, and kept you all in such comfort.' Her eyes scan the room again, her face in shock at the contrast. We wait for Mother's reaction. Ada, clutching my arm now, has tears streaming down her cheeks. Mother's face is impassive.

'Kasama was jealous. He wrote it all in this letter.' She shakily searches her pocket for a letter, though one does not emerge. 'He took his own life a few weeks ago, he left me a note, saying he was sorry. He couldn't live with what he had done. The pressure of work got to him in the end, he worked so hard. He was jealous of your man's promotion. He thought he had made a clean cut, but then your husband got away. You need to know the truth. You have suffered so, so much, Maria. I am so sorry I can't help you.' She finishes, her body shaking with fresh sobs.

Mother, to our astonishment, remains mute. She gently pulls her to her feet and draws the woman close to her swollen chest and holds her in her arms, the way I have always wanted her to hold me. Just like that, Mother forgives her. Ada still sobs, Hope looks sick. I think about everything we have been through as a family. If it wasn't for Kasama our old Taata would still be here. We would all be well fed, healthy, happy, educated. Each of us would have a future. I want to hit her, so she will get a taste of the daily beatings I get from the Lout. Are we better off knowing? I could not say. Despite the violence that bubbles deep within me, I know that this sad woman is not to blame. The murderer has suffered on his part, and God would not want me to take it upon myself.

Chapter Twenty-Five

We are still awaiting some kind of outburst from Maama. Last night she and Kasama's wife said their goodbyes quietly in the front yard. She ate a little when she returned to the house. She sat, silently, eating alongside us. We all reached for whatever we wanted and were never told to save any for him. After supper, she collapsed on to her mattress, alongside the sleeping Elizabeth, and she too fell into deep sleep.

Ada and I had not seen her sleeping so deeply since we left our old life. Maybe she was at peace, knowing the truth at long last. Both she and Elizabeth slept all night and it is only now, with the return of Taata, that she is awake.

He has come home with fire in his belly. He never made it to prayers last night, the siren call of the bar was too strong. I smell the alcohol before he has even drawn the curtain. These sessions end in one of three ways. He either returns to pass out (usually after vomiting first), to rape Mother, or to fight.

'Woman, get up, where is my dinner?'

She sits up serenely. She looks his way with complete indifference. She simply strokes the baby's hair and lies down again.

'I said, where the *hell* is my dinner, *woman*?' He swears through his teeth and I begin shaking where I am lying, pretending I have not woken.

She sits up again, wearily.

'Dinner is a meal served in the evening. It is now morning, allowing an enquiry about breakfast. If you wanted dinner, then you should have come home last night.'

'What do you say to me?'

Mother rolls her eyes.

'Deaf now, as well as stupid?' She mutters, loud enough for him to hear her and rises from the mattress slowly, her hand resting on her stomach, still protruding after the birth.

'Stupid?' He spits.

'Keep talking if you must, someday you might say something intelligent.'

145

He is so shocked that he slumps into a chair. 'Get me some dinner, woman. You are here to cook for me and serve me, that is all.'

I am so afraid for her, but so proud that she is finally standing up to him.

'You speak to me like that, woman, and you can leave this house, hear me? You and all your bastard children.'

'Maybe we shall do just that. Then you can sit here alone, playing with yourself, eating scraps and drinking milk, like the miserable excuse for a man that you are. I should know. I used to be married to a real one.'

I am electrified, still too afraid to move, to let on that I have heard every word. He is still drunk. He is bewildered, not used to being forced to face the truth. He is too stung to retaliate. Mother leaves the room for the latrine. Juliet, Hope and Elizabeth remain soundly asleep. We are so vulnerable. He could kill us all before Mother even gets back. But he barely looks at us. His rage has slumped out of him. He knows full well that what Mother says is true. He kicks off his sandals. He surveys the mattress but decides against it. Returning the sandals to his feet, he slowly shuffles out.

By the time he returns we are having breakfast, some of the leftovers from last night along with fruit and water. He has a bottle of milk under one arm and nods at us as he enters. He still smells of alcohol, but his nasty little dose of truth has sobered him up. He sits beside Mother, who asks me to pass him some fruit. We eat quietly. Mother's face is sad. Even Juliet cannot raise a smile.

'School today?' Taata enquires.

I am astonished he could even ask. We have not been to school for months.

'We owe money to every school in Bwaise,' Mother responds.

Taata nods sadly. He has no fight left in him. Mother divides the last of her breakfast between Hope and Juliet, who whoop in delight. Taata watches as she rises, confusion written over his face. He has no clue what has caused the change in her. Bullies thrive on weakness, and she has found strength. Mother folds some of Elizabeth's tiny clothes, tosses the blankets around, tidying ineffectually. Outside the sky rumbles, a storm is coming in, at last breaking the long string of hot, humid weather. Hope squeals excitedly and runs to the door to look out for the rain. Mother lies down again, and feeds Elizabeth lazily while lying on her side. I clear up the breakfast things. Taata is not yelling or abusing us. Mother is not making snide remarks, the girls, for once, are not cowering in terror. I am afraid it is the calm before the storm.

The rain finally started to fall a week ago, and we are thoroughly sick of it. At first it washed away the dust and gave us a reprieve from the oppressive heat, but now everything is damp, everything smells mouldy and the novelty has well and truly worn off. The dusty streets are mud-ridden, stray dogs cower under doorways, children too, wanting to play ball again. Our house is littered with wet laundry, baby clothes and nappies, with nowhere to dry them out. Mother is more irritable than usual. My sisters and I have been ordered to wave the cloth nappies around to dry them off, but it's like spitting in a cyclone. Even the walls of our tiny home are damp. Mother swears and returns to the mattress, pulling up corners of bedding, pushing our bags to one side, hoping to find something, anything dry for the baby. She swears again. I glance at her irritably and want to demand what on earth she fancies complaining about now. Her body is bent in two and her eyelids are screwed tightly together. She supports herself against the sodden concrete wall.

Suddenly Mother collapses onto the mattress and screams in agony, clutching at her stomach. I run to her, though she is in too much pain to tell us what is wrong. Taata enters. Elizabeth wails, frightened by the noise, Juliet too, but Maama's screams drown them out. Taata looks panicked. He throws a hooded top over his head and runs out into the rain. I try to remain calm for the younger ones, but I am terrified. Mother is still screaming as I put a cold compress on her brow, which is drenched in sweat. She is writhing in agony, and she shakes me off each time I reapply it. It seems wrong to do nothing when she is so distressed.

147

Taata comes back with Beatrice.

'Do something, Beatrice,' I plead, 'Help her.'

Beatrice orders Taata to fetch a neighbour. It is not hard to find one, as they are all gathered on the street outside, not wanting to miss out on the drama. Someone is nominated to look after the babies, then Beatrice, Taata and I use our combined weight to levy Mother to her feet. She is in too much pain to stand; her body is a dead weight. We move her slowly towards the door. I am directed to go ahead and alert a matatu. God is with me; I find one immediately.

'Mulago hospital' I order the driver, who helps us to lay Mother down on one of the seats. She is retching with the pain, but the driver looks unconcerned. Sickness is something the people of Kampala are used to seeing. He puts his foot down and steers the vehicle in and out of the crowds. The rain has made the road bumpier than ever. Mother screams as the tyres bounce on the potholes. The journey is never-ending. Crowds of shoppers gather at the markets, blocking the traffic, the usual stray animals and wayward children throng the streets. I pray to God under my breath to just get us there.

At last the huge hospital looms in front of us. It is an ugly concrete monstrosity with blue detailing, but I have never been more grateful to see anything in my life. The driver pulls up beside a maze of blue railing, leading towards the entrance. It seems a long way to walk with Maama.

'Help us,' Taata urges the driver.

'It is not my job,' he says as he snatches the fare from Taata and drives away.

We slowly ease Mother towards the doors. We struggle under her weight and use the railings to pull ourselves closer. Every few feet large, repulsive looking birds stubbornly hold their position along the bar. They are Kaloli birds, known as the undertakers. They are here for a reason. Over the side of one of the railings a body lies face down, along with abandoned rubbish and hospital waste at the side of an overflowing tip. A horde of the hideous creatures fight over the decaying flesh, feeding greedily. I want to heave, but Mother needs me. I focus on the front door and edge slowly forward, attempting to steady my shaking legs.

'A doctor. My wife needs a doctor,' Taata shouts as we eventually pull her into the entrance. His voice is lost in a sea of people. There are hordes of them, sitting or lying wherever they can, some curled up like Mother, screaming in pain, others vomiting into bags or containers. A woman is sweating in a corner, shaking with fever. She has no one to help her, and she has soiled herself. Tiny, bony babies wail as they throw their limbs wherever they can reach. Some have family members, like us, there for moral support, but many don't, their belongings scattered around them in large bags, looking as if they have travelled miles to be here and now, they must wait to be seen.

Beatrice and Taata gently rest Mother against the wall. She is delirious, flitting in and out of consciousness, and has vomited down her dress. Taata goes to find someone. A large lady with a clipboard shakes her head at him. He returns to speak to Beatrice.

'Do you have money?'

'No, none,'

'She will not be seen if we can't pay.'

'How much?'

'The more we have the quicker she will be seen.'

We wait. And we wait. I notice a pattern. A man in a smart jacket rises casually and follows a doctor who has just called for him. The doctors ignore the desperately ill and dying, and the poor souls in agony, like Mother. He probably has a slight cough or an ingrown toenail. What he has, that we do not, is money. I hope he has really painful haemorrhoids, I think viciously. The lady next to us is clutching a baby who looks close to death. The mother's eyes have glazed over in grief and panic. Her lips are cracked but move rapidly, muttering to her baby to stay alive. She does not cry, she barely moves. Her chest moves up and down as though each breath is a struggle, yet they are ignored, presumably as she has no money either.

Mother stirs and vomits again. I mop it up with one of Elizabeth's nappies.

'I will go and get money. Stay with her,' Taata announces. Beatrice urges him to hurry.

He scurries through the door. Beatrice strokes the top of my head. 'Oh Lela, child.' But we have nothing useful to say to each other.

We sit side by side, muttering the odd word of comfort to Mother. I only hope she will never remember this moment. People around us come and go. I am so relieved when the mother and her baby are called in. I wonder if that baby will ever go home.

At last Taata reappears. It is dark outside now. I have lost all track of time.

'What took you so long?' Beatrice whispers fiercely.

'I have been everywhere. I still need more, but this should help for now.' He hands over ten thousand Ugandan shillings. Beatrice takes them but looks concerned.

'It is not enough.'

'I know, I will be back.' He leaves and Beatrice shudders.

She looks at Mother, who is slumped over, catatonic, her clothes thick with sweat. I smell something awful and wonder if she has soiled herself, like the lady in the corner. She doesn't seem to have noticed if she has. Beatrice takes the money and shows it to the woman with the clipboard. At last Mother is called. I thank God under my breath as Beatrice and I help the doctor move her to a ward.

Chapter Twenty-Six

I should be grateful that Mother has a bed at all, but it is one of dozens in row after row with very little room between each. Close to Mother's bed a young woman is vomiting uncontrollably into a bowl. I try and close off my ears, my eyes, my nose, but the horror of it makes me want to heave too. The ward smells of urine and vomit mixed with an overpowering smell of body odour, completely drowning out any hint of disinfectant. Mother too is vomiting. I mop it up myself as best I can, as there is no one else to do it.

Beatrice is anxious to get back to her children.

'Go,' I say to her. She looks uncomfortable.

'Your Taata hasn't returned.'

'He is not my Taata,' I say quietly.

'I should wait. Speak to the doctor.'

'Beatrice, you are such a good friend to us, but you need to return to your children.'

She leans forward to kiss the top of my head.

'Oh Lela, if only you had been allowed to be a child,' she says sadly.

Beatrice does not argue any longer though. She whispers something quietly into Mother's ear, strokes her hair a few times and fights her way through the crowded ward. I wished I too could get out of there. I pull myself onto the metal bed and snuggle closer to my sleeping Maama. She looks so frail, her eyes and fingers flickering simultaneously, her breathing, raspy, breaking in places. There are moments I fear she has stopped breathing altogether, and then it begins again. My body feels weary, but I do not wish to sleep, in case she needs me. The ward grows quieter. I am grateful that the young woman has stopped vomiting. The room is filled mainly with women, although there are a few men on one side. The women, like Mother, are not alone. Some of them have masses of children, with nowhere else to go. Some sleep on the bed alongside their mothers, others squeeze into the space below the bed, between the slats and the floor, curled up in whatever way they can to find a little comfort.

Mother stirs. Her head is hotter than it was before, her murmurings incoherent. I sit up, on the lookout for a doctor or nurse. They have given Mother some pain killers, but her fever is raging. I see a nurse down the hallway, so I creep out of bed and tiptoe between the sleeping bodies. The nurse is working fast, her tunic covered in blood. She pays me no attention as she darts from one room to another. I follow her on her rounds, trying to speak to her, until she grows tired of the sight of me.

'What girl? What? Why you follow me?'

'My mother is very sick.'

'Well then she is in the right place.'

'She is very hot; she burns with a fever.'

'I suspect she does. The doctor has seen her and now she must wait until his rounds tomorrow. You can help her by keeping her cool, remove her blankets, dab her with water if you can locate some that is clean. We must all do our bit.' She turns away and is gone.

As I try to find my way back, I realise I am lost. Most of the rooms are in darkness now. I enter a room full of children, their beds packed even more tightly than the adult ones. In a little crib nearest the door I see the baby from the waiting room. She is still with us, but there are tubes coming in and out of her. Her breathing is still troubled. Beside her, curled in a ball lies her mother, her eyes fixed on her baby. My heart hurts for her.

At last I find Mother. She still sleeps a restless sleep. I do not have anything to dab her with, the rag is heavy with vomit. I rip a piece of cloth from my dress and wet it from a basin near the door. I slowly dab Mother's head, face, neck and chest. Her fever remains, but she seems more comfortable. She calls for Taata (my good, kind Taata, rather than the Lout), then returns to a fitful slumber.

I follow the example of the other children and make a bed for myself under Mother's. The floor is hard and cold, and I fear the noises. Patients call out in pain and people scream down the hall. Mother is so sick. What if she doesn't make the night? I shudder at the thought. I am chilly in my simple dress and the floor only makes it worse. A corner of Mother's sheet hangs from her bed and I snuggle up against it, but there is barely enough to cover my cheek. Somehow, I drift in and out of sleep between the cries, the vomiting, the bed pans, and I am so grateful when the sun starts rising.

The ward is quieter than it was in darkness. A few children whine for breakfast, but the adults remain still. I crawl out from under the bed to check on Mother. Her forehead feels cooler and she sleeps more soundly. I take the opportunity to find the toilet then return and watch the sun rising over the city. I have never seen the sunrise from so high up, so used to being low, near the gutter. From here I can see over houses, see the sunshine glinting in windows. For a moment I am transfixed and forget my location, until a nurse bustles into the ward. She heads for Mother.

'How did she sleep?' She enquires. It is the same nurse I found during the night.

'She shouted a lot but seems calmer now.'

'See this?' She points at a bag full of clear fluid. 'This is a drip. It keeps your mother hydrated. She is too sick to drink, so it always needs to have liquid in it. I am too busy to keep an eye on it all the time, so you need to help, understand?'

I nod.

'When it gets empty, you call me.'

'Ok.' As if on cue Mother retches in her sleep. She brings up a little fluid, murmurs and then snores loudly. The nurse rolls her eyes.

'We can't leave her like that?' I stare.

'This, child, will also be your job. You see how many people we need to look after. Sheets are down the hall. Follow me. I will show you how to change the bed while she is in it, and where to put the dirty linen, but the rest is down to you.'

I listen intently, suddenly aware that I will not be going home anytime soon. Not that it is much of a home. The idea of being in the shack with Taata alone terrifies me. I think of my sisters. I hope they are still with our kind neighbour. I change the sheets and mop up Mother. My stomach grumbles. I have had nothing to eat since yesterday's measly breakfast.

By mid-morning there is a steady flow of people in and out of the crowded ward; visitors, nurses, doctors, and children playing, despite the warnings from the staff. I crane

153

my neck on the lookout for Taata. I never thought I'd be pleased to see him, but we need more money. Finally, Beatrice arrives, a herd of children at her feet.

'I collected them last night,' Beatrice explains as she sees my expression. 'He had not returned when I went to check on them.' She rocks Elizabeth in her arms, the child fidgets uncomfortably, wanting her Maama's breast, and begins to wail. Beatrice looks exhausted.

'They will have to stay here, Lela. I'm sorry, I can't look after them all as well as my own. I am sick too.'

I can see for myself how gaunt Beatrice has become.

'Of course, Beatrice,' I take Elizabeth from her arms.

'I have brought some food. It's not much but should get you through the day. There are bottles in there too to give Elizabeth some milk if your mother cannot feed, and here, this is all the money I could find, hopefully your Taa... your stepfather will bring more soon.' She sounds convincing, but her face is creased with lines of worry.

I am terrified, but I do not show it. How can I look after my sisters and help with Mother too? Beatrice takes my face in her hands.

'No matter what anyone has said to you Lela, you are an incredible person. I will visit when I can, but it is difficult, understand?'

'Yes.'

'Ada works hard, and will send whatever spare money she can too, but she doesn't earn much, and she helps support my kids. You are both good girls, your Mother should be proud.'

I know she isn't.

Beatrice gives me a tight hug. I can barely breathe and want to tell her she is suffocating me when I realise she is hugging me goodbye.

'Do you have what Maama has?'

Beatrice nods sadly.

'Is Maama going to die?'

'I don't know sweetie, I don't know.'

'Are you going to die?'

'I'll do my best not to.'

She gathers her own children, briefly kissing my sisters on their heads and turns to leave. She tries to hide it, but she is

154

crying. I want to cry too, but I bundle my sisters under the bed instead.

'This is our home now, get it?' Hope looks around her, her eyes wide. Juliet sucks her thumb, a habit she has picked up since moving in with Taata. Elizabeth is briefly pacified with a bottle. I warn them all that they must stay under the bed, stay safe, stay out of trouble. If they make a nuisance of themselves, I fear that the doctors will throw them out onto the street. I am not sure if I am able to drum the message into them. For now, at least, they seem scared enough by their strange location, seeing Mother so sick, seeing the other men and women ill around them. But I've learned that children can grow used to just about anything, and if they don't behave, I will be unable to protect them.

Chapter Twenty-Seven

The hunger gnaws at my stomach. Every now and then it cramps painfully, as it contains only acid. Beatrice's money dried up fast. Every time my mother's drip ran out, I had to hand over more cash to get her topped up. It's been a week now and I have given up hope of 'Taata' returning. Probably spending what he could scrounge in the bar.

Mother seems improved. To spare her feelings, I told her that her husband came while she was sleeping, but I see in her eyes she knows he has abandoned us.

My job is to keep Mother clean. She is in constant pain and she is ill on herself often. I am getting used to it now. She has stopped yelling at me, stopped calling me names. Instead she seems relieved to have me by her side. In moments of lucidity she begs me to be careful, telling me that the sheets could kill me, make me sick too, and not to get any on my hands. I do not have gloves, I must risk it, but I know she is right. If I got sick, who would look after my sisters? I reassure her that I'm fine, not to worry, and then she usually drifts back to sleep. It is true, I feel well, all except the clenching hunger. The little ones cry around me.

'I am so hungry Lela,' Hope lies, curled in a ball under the bed, clutching her little empty belly. I stroke her hair, but I have no words for her. The children around me fight for scraps as their parents lie incapacitated. There is nothing for us here. I think back to the day we arrived. It seems a million years ago now. I think of the smart man in the waiting room, paying his wad of cash to be seen immediately. There are no rich people in this ward. We are the dregs of society. I bet there is a whole wing in a big hospital like this, where they have private rooms and hot meals.

'Wait here,' I order.

'Where are you going?'

'We need to eat.' I slowly walk out of the ward. When they first came, I had worried about them running around, getting thrown out. But they are all so weak with hunger now that I do not need to worry about them moving an inch. I keep out of the way of the nurses, staying close to the walls, away from the beds being wheeled around with blood stained sheets and wailing people. The hospital corridors are endless; many, many wards like Mother's, crowded with poverty. I find some stairs and make my way up one floor, and then another, until I see a row of men in smart trousers and suits, awaiting some sort of clinic. They all ignore me as I approach. One is standing. He turns his back on me altogether. Instead I edge closer to the ones who are seated, more in my eyeline. I hope they find this harder to ignore. I stare until a man with a bald head catches my eye.

'What do you want, girl?'

'My mother is sick, and we have nothing to eat.'

'Leave off, I have no food.'

'But maybe money so I can buy some?' I am overcome with shame as he stares at me. For a second, I fear he wishes to hit me, but then he sighs, shakes his head and digs in his pocket. He finds a few pennies and throws them my way.

'Now leave me alone.'

'Thank you, sir.' I remember to be polite and try a few of the other men in the waiting area. Only two or three more take pity on me but it is enough. I find a small canteen, serving mainly doctors. My money does not go far but it is enough for one plate of hot food, a bit of fruit and some milk for Elizabeth. The portion is big enough to feed my sisters and they drift into a quiet sleep. Mother too manages a little rice, squashed up so she doesn't have to chew.

'Thank you,' she strokes my face and she too sleeps. I manage with the scraps. We will all be hungry again soon. I watch the clock as the others rest, wondering how quick the turnover is in that clinic with the rich people. I decide to chance my luck, but I am disappointed to see that it is almost empty now. The stairs have worn me out. My body is so weak with hunger. I am wondering if I will breathe in fresh air again. I take a seat and sigh, thinking through my options. If I turn down this corridor, or that one, will there be another ward full of rich people?

'You, child, come here.' I have been so consumed by my thoughts I have not noticed a man leaving his office. I am taken aback by his appearance. He is obviously a doctor, standing tall in his white coat and stethoscope hanging from his neck. His skin is the whitest I have ever seen, his cheeks pink. His hair, too, very short and yellow, like the sunshine. I want to be polite, to answer, but all I can do is stare, and try and put off the strange urge to go and stroke him, to see if his skin feels the same as mine.

'What is your name?' His voice is gentle, as he approaches me. Despite the urge to touch him I find myself recoiling as he comes closer.

'Do not be afraid, I saw you here earlier, asking for money.' I hang my head in shame. I want to explain, but I cannot even look him in the eye.

'You must be very hungry huh?' He feels around in his pocket and pulls out a bar of candy.

'Here, take this. My wife wouldn't be happy if she found out I was eating candy,' he sniggers.

I tentatively take the chocolate from his hand. I do not wish to embarrass myself further, but I am so hungry that I tear the packet open and take great mouthfuls.

'Your Mother is here? Or your father?'

'Mother.' I muffle with full cheeks.

'Do you have brothers or sisters?'

'I do, my sisters are here too, like me, except Ada,' I manage once I have swallowed my mouthful.

'You do not have any money?'

To my horror, I begin to cry. I have been so busy looking after Mother, and the girls, and trying to find food I have not allowed myself to fathom how stressful it all is. To have a kind face looking at me, asking me about my problems, makes it all come to the surface.

'I know, it's hard, it's ok to cry. Hospitals make me want to do that too.'

He places his arm around my shoulder.

'My name is Harry, Harry Talisman. I would like to help you, if I can. Please take me to your Mother.'

I wipe my tears and lead the way down the empty halls of upstairs to the crowded, infested lower floors. I find my family still napping. Mother stirs at the voice of the kindly doctor.

'Lela, you watch your sisters for a moment, I wish to speak to your Mother alone.'

I crawl under the bed. I can easily hear what they say, but do not understand the words that are used. Harry offers to help my Mother get medicines. He is a missionary, doing God's work, and he can help pay for the drugs she needs and for the food we require. I raise my eyes towards the underside of the bed and thank God under my breath. I have learnt He works in mysterious ways but will always send help if He can. This time, He has sent Harry.

Chapter Twenty-Eight

Mother shows improvement daily. Harry Talisman sends a nurse every morning to administer medicines that we would not be able to afford without his help. She is now able to eat proper meals, sit up in bed, and is no longer soiling herself. Our relationship grows stronger too. Without a man around to impress she is kinder, more caring, and thankful for everything I have done. I treasure her thanks.

It is shortly after breakfast. Mother has had her shot from the nurse and the younger children still doze under the bed, the day young. Summer is in the air and the mornings are bright, lighting the whole ward in golden sunshine. On days like today it is almost possible to forget where you are. Now Mother is growing stronger I can take my sisters outside for short periods of fresh air. Harry gives us pocket money to spend occasionally and there are a few shops selling sweet cakes, mandazis and fruit on the opposite side of the street, where we can choose something to share. I am hoping today may be one of those days. The air looks inviting.

'Shots,' a voice calls behind me, making me jump. A large matron, with a huge bust and freckled nose bustles into the ward. She pushes a trolley with the biggest needles I have ever seen lined up in a row. Six altogether. I turn my attention away to tend to Elizabeth, who cries for a bottle. As Elizabeth suckles noisily, I watch the matron edge her way to the beds, all filled with mothers like my own, quietly trying to recover whilst hiding armies of little ones under the bed. Some of the women quibble at the jab, they do not have the money to pay for it, but the matron insists that they have been sent to this ward particularly and the doctor in charge has requested them, so not to argue. She pushes the women onto their sides, prepping the needles and tapping the sides before sticking them into the tops of their skinny, sickly arms. The women flinch and rub the injection spot. I do not imagine a woman of such a size knows how to be gentle. When all but one injection has been used, she heads over to Mother.

'Arm,' she demands.

'I'm sorry, what is this shot?' Mother asks, confused. We know her meds routine, and this is not it.

'Doctor's orders. I must do you like the others,' she nods at the woman across the aisle, still rubbing her arm and giving evil glances at the matron.

'Mother has had a shot today, ordered by Harry Talisman,' I offer.

'Talisman, you say?' The matron consults her clipboard.

'Yes, he is Mother's doctor now,' I insist.

'Hmm, alright, I will hold off until I've spoken to his nurse.'

She pushes her squeaky trolley back down the aisle and along the hall, the wheels still audible long after she is out of sight. The ward returns to its sleepy early morning malaise, the youngest children sharing scraps under the beds. I close my eyes as a sunbeam flits across my brow, knowing the kids will be ready to play shortly and my relaxation time will be over.

'Maama, Maama, what's wrong?' It's a panicked child across the ward. A young girl, no older that Hope sits on top of her Mother. Her Mother has not responded well to the terrifying jab. I have seen this before. Sometimes they get allergic reactions. It isn't pretty, but another shot usually sorts them out. A second, younger child flees the ward in search of a nurse. Whilst these occurrences are distressing, it is a hospital, and they are more than commonplace. The girl continues to shake her Mother, now floppy in her arms. My heart catches as the girl sobs into her mother's chest, pleading with her to wake. Why does the nurse not return?

I notice that the woman across the aisle is suffering too. Her eyes have rolled back into her head, bright white balls deep within her black skin. Her hands clasp at her throat, as though she is strangling herself. She makes a muffled choking sound, and gurgles alarmingly. Her children cry at her side. Mother sits up, her back poker straight, eyes staring. Her right arm reaches up to grasp mine as we both look on in disbelief. The rest of the ward is shaken too, those who are able call loudly for nurses, while the children crowd at the entrance of the hallway, not knowing which direction to turn.

'What is wrong? Mother stop it, Maama!' The children become increasingly distressed. The woman closest to us is convulsing violently, white foamy saliva erupts from her mouth like lava. Her eldest mops at it, either to help stop the convulsions or to retain her mother's dignity, it isn't clear, but as quickly as they began the convulsions stop. Mother and I watch in horror as the woman suddenly slumps, mouth wide open, arms dropping down the side of her bed. She is absolutely still.

Mother's grip on my arm tightens. She gazes in shock at yet another victim. A third has suffered the same fate and lies deadly still. She is alone in the ward and she has simply passed on without recognition. Mother panics.

'Lela, we need to leave. Help me, help me.' Both hands reach for me so I can pull her to her feet. I try and get her up but her body, still weak, drops to the ground.

'Lela, a wheelchair, I need a wheelchair.' I leave Mother on the floor; a crowd has gathered around the beds and I am reluctant to leave her in such a vulnerable position, but her safety is at stake. I manoeuvre my way through the crowds, heading down the hallway in search of a discarded wheelchair. As I reach the X-ray unit, I see one parked outside one of the consulting rooms, while its occupant is tended to on the X-ray table. I am as casual as possible, although my heart is racing. I examine the posters with furious interest whilst two doctors pass, deep in conversation about the distressing AIDS epidemic. It's not the first time I've heard the word. Once they are gone, I grab the wheelchair and run back towards the ward. I barge my way back through the crowds just as an ear-piercing screech fills the room. A fourth woman is down. From her daughter's screams I know she is dead. Hope and I lift Mother from the floor, her frail body shaking uncontrollably with fear.

'Find Harry,' she orders, 'he can help.'

I plonk Elizabeth onto Mother's lap. The little ones chase after me as I force the chair through the hordes of people, many still craning their necks as the spectacle unfolds. Others gather their own children together for escape. I am unsure where the lifts are, so we chase up and down several long halls, each time turning our backs to change direction as we see nurses on their rounds, desperately hoping that they are too busy to notice us. At last we find a solitary elevator, with a queue of nurses and hospital workers pushing trolleys and beds. I want to turn from them, but some instinct tells me that showing no fear will let us bluff our way through. The lift is small, so several trips leave before we edge nearer to the front of a queue. A man is watching us closely. I pretend to be deep in conversation with Hope about Elizabeth, lying peacefully in Mother's arms, oblivious to the drama.

'Can I help you? Are you lost?' he enquires.

'No fine, thank you,' I reply, Mother looks increasingly sick as the adrenaline rush takes hold of her frail frame.

'What floor are you heading to?' He continues as the lift returns for more passengers.

'Five please,' I insist.

'Testicular cancer?' He raises his eyebrows in concern.

'We have an appointment with Mr. Talisman,' I continue.

'Today?'

'Yes, he is Mother's doctor. Now she is feeling better he requests we visit him in his office, he thinks it will help improve her strength.' She doesn't look strong. Her hands are shaking, and she slumps to one side with exhaustion.

'You must be mistaken. He is not in hospital on Thursday, as he does his rounds through the slums.'

'Oh Thursday, umm, oh yes, you're right. I thought it was Friday.' I casually begin reversing. He is still suspicious, but he decides he has better things to do than harass a group of females and gets into the lift and is gone.

'Now what?'

'We need get out of here, Lela,' Mother stammers.

'Yes, but to go where?'

'Home.'

'Home? Taata has abandoned us. We do not have a home to go to.'

'Run to your reverend friend, the man who gave us the food. See if he can help us leave this awful place.'

'You are not well enough, Mother.'

'If I stay here, I will die. Please go.'

164

I leave her in the chair, surrounded by my crying sisters, but I do as she asks. I run as fast as my legs will carry me, down the stairs, through the electric doors and into the city. The streets quickly turn from dusty concrete high rises, to dirty sandy shacks, corrugated iron and open sewage flowing through the streets, and I know I am almost back at our tiny shack. The entrance is boarded up. I pray Father Silver is at church. It is further than I remember. The day is half gone by the time I reach it, but to my intense relief he is there.

My message to him is garbled. Sooner or later someone will return Mother to her bed. What if a lethal injection is waiting for her?

It takes several attempts to tell him what is going on, but my obvious panic does the trick. He gives me money to get back to the hospital and bring my family back. He goes in search of the landlord of the shack. My relief at seeing my Mother and sisters huddled on the top step is indescribable. Someone has kicked her out of the wheelchair. I rage at who would do such a thing. Probably the rich wastrel with the ingrown toenail. Mother is slumped against the wall and Hope is trying to deal with a screaming Elizabeth and an exhausted Juliet. It is time to get home.

Father Silver waits in the entrance of our tiny shack, the door no longer boarded. He rushes to our aid as Mother collapses out of the transport. She nods her appreciation, the first smidgeon of gratitude she has ever shown him. He carries her to the mattress, still in the same place we left it so many weeks ago on that rainy morning when she fell ill. She falls asleep immediately. The stress of the day has almost been enough to kill her, but her medication from Harry has certainly eased her suffering. As Father Silver settles her, I cannot help but look around our surroundings. The mattress is still there, yes, but all other signs of life have vanished. The moth-eaten chair is missing, just a pile of dust in its place, the wall hangings also vanished. I crane my neck to see if our belongings remain in the so-called bedroom, but 'Taata' has made off with everything. My little cardboard suitcase has gone, my bible, my scraps of clothing. I remind myself to be grateful. Mother is still with us, my sisters are here too, and kind people have helped us in so many ways. Most of all, we may be back here, but the Lout has gone. Maybe now, at long last, we can work properly at being a family.

Chapter Twenty-Nine

'Lela, do you think your God loves me?'

Our stay at home was short lived. We are back in hospital now, although a different one. Beatrice sent us to TASO, an organisation that helped with her sickness, and they put us here, Entebbe 4B. The dry season is ending already. I have spent all my time caring for Mother. Each evening grows a little colder and I am, as usual, huddled in a ball under Mother's bed. I'm so surprised that I ask her to repeat her question, in case I had misheard.

'Do you think your God loves me?'

'Yes, of course, he loves all his children.'

'And I, am I one of his children?' she enquires.

'We all are.'

'Will he forgive me?'

'Mother, what troubles you so?'

'This disease, Lela, the one that burdens me so, it is my punishment. I think your God punishes me.'

I shake my head, not willing to believe that my God could punish someone I love so dearly, despite her flaws.

'I have done so many things I'm not proud of and this sickness is my punishment. I have AIDS, Lela, do you know what this is?'

I do not know, not fully, but have learned a little about it just by listening to the doctors, who talk freely in front of me, assuming I can't understand.

'They will get you better, won't they?' I cling onto the hope that maybe miracles do happen.

Mother smiles solemnly. Her face gives me my answer.

'Make me a promise, Lela.'

'Of course, Mother.'

'Call me Maama, Lela, my girl,' My eyes are swamped with tears, they rush to my eyes at her words and I fight to keep them back. This is what I have wished for my whole life. She takes my hand in hers, softly, and tenderly kisses each of my fingertips. I am fearful this moment will soon be gone forever.

'Look after the others, won't you, your sisters. Your grandmother, my Mother, find her. If anything happens to me, find her.'

'Nothing will happen to you. This is a good hospital. They will work to get you well again, Maama.' My voice is strangely high pitched, and my throat closes up.

Maama says, 'I love you, my girl, you are a good child.'

I cannot hold back my tears. I hope in the darkness of the ward they cannot be seen, but she loosens my grip on her hand and raises one finger to catch a tear, then brings it to her own mouth to kiss it.

'Will you pray with me, Lela? Teach me one of your prayers, and then maybe God will help us both, help me to become strong once more, help us both to live a life we can be proud of.'

My mind is blank, too tormented at the thought of losing my own Mother. I attempt to create a prayer, to thank God for the doctors, or Father Silver, Harry Talisman, or each other, but I am rendered speechless. Instead I think of the only prayer I learnt at church and so begin reciting it, Maama joining in as I repeat it for her.

Our Father, who art in Heaven,
Hallowed be thy name,
Thy Kingdom come,
Thy will be done,
On earth,
As it is in Heaven.
Give us this day our daily bread,
And forgive us our trespasses,
As we forgive those that trespass against us.
And lead us not into temptation,
But deliver us from evil.
For thine is the kingdom,
The power and the glory,
For ever and ever.
Amen.

'Such beautiful words,' she murmurs. We hold hands until we both drift to sleep. In the morning, I am awake before her, still holding her hand in mine. She sleeps calmly, her breathing steady and I am grateful. Once she wakes, she is too sick to speak again. The feeding tube goes in, her throat becomes raw. Instead of further kind words she gives me her tears, her tears when she sees me sad, her tears as I change her bed. I wish to make her laugh, just one more time, but her final days are soaked in tears.

September the fourteenth in the year 2000 dawns; golden, sunny and warm. A day made for celebration rather than sorrow. But as I crawl out from under the bed I am overwhelmed by silence. I am used to the raspy noise of Mother's breathing, trying to inhale the oxygen pumped through her tubes. The quiet is unbearable. My bare feet inch nearer to her on the tiles. My hand hovers over her naked arm, avoiding the drips and drains, but I do not dare touch her. My eyes fixate on her chest, willing it to rise, but she is still. I allow my arm to drop to my side once more.

'Please God, just one more minute, let me say goodbye,' but I know that God has already given me the time I had prayed for. I am heavy with the weight of decay, disease, desolation. Yet those days had been ours. Here in Entebbe 4B it was just me and her. The little ones are being cared for by Beatrice and the missionary workers at TASO. I was alone with my Maama, and I had finally seen that she had grown to truly love me.

The hospital is waking up. Nurses are on the early morning rounds; doctors are changing shifts. I know I should alert them. How could she die in the night without me noticing? Could I have saved her? I fervently wish I hadn't slept.

At last I allow myself to touch her skin, almost as cold as the floor I stand on. I'm overwhelmed with shame for the colossal anger I feel towards her. I want to scream at her. She has abandoned me *again*. Why did you ever leave me, Maama? First you left me with Iris. Iris invited Mussa. Did you know about Mussa? Then you stood by and did nothing as Taata beat me, strangled me so my eyes almost popped out of my head. My face is getting hotter, my fists clenched, my body is shaking, but as quickly as the rage surged, it subsides. My eyes refocus on the shadow of the woman I knew. Just her skin and bones are left. She was decomposing before she even died. I take her fingertips and bring them to my own lips, kissing each lightly as she had done with me during our final conversation. The nurse enters the ward. She instantly recognises the look on my face. She has seen it many times. She strokes my shoulder, once, then again, and she turns away to close off the drips, pull out the drains. I respect her silence. She knows that words are empty. I kiss my mother's forehead. The last thing she ever said to me was the Lord's prayer. This shows me how much God must love her, and it comforts me in the days to come.

I walk out of that ward for the last time, alone, left to fend for myself.

Chapter Thirty

We come home with our dead Mother. The house has been leaking now that the rains have returned, and the mattress is sodden. The air is hot and humid, and the slums are filled with the stench of sewage. The hospital was kind enough to pay for the transport to get her home, but we do not know what to do with her body in these rank conditions. The TASO workers informed Beatrice of Mother's death, and Grandmother, Maama's mother, as she had wished. The women, along with Ada, now fuss around, arguing. My grandmother, Jaaja is crying at the loss of her daughter, at an illness she knew nothing of, at grandchildren she had not seen often enough.

They worry that Mother's body will start to smell with the heat and the damp. My sisters and I are ordered to find banana leaves in the plantation. We are grateful for something to do, to get away from the house with so many bad memories, to escape death. We run through the banana groves, hiding behind trees and jumping out on each other. My sisters laugh, but my heart is grieving. Not just for the loss of our mother. What will become of us?

Once we have returned with the banana leaves, we are scolded for taking so long, but then we are hugged, for obvious reasons. We are told to take the extra banana leaves outside and use them to make our own beds. The thought of sleeping outside in the open in the slums would have scared me once, but the ones called family are usually more terrifying than strangers. I prefer to be outside than sleep next to a dead body. My sisters are afraid to say so, but they clearly agree. Jaaja and Beatrice move Maama's body to a bed of banana leaves in the centre of the room, every now and then turning her slightly to air her before she is buried. We should have buried her straight away, but Beatrice said we need to give people time to say their goodbyes in their own way. Who wants to say goodbye to a rotting corpse? Sometimes I honestly think that grown-ups are crazy. Beatrice's eyes keep straying to the door. I wonder if she looks for Taata, returning to wish his wife farewell. I am certain we shall not see him again and I am not sorry. Perhaps he has AIDS too. I think of all the times he beat us and abused and raped Mother, and I feel a vicious lick of pleasure unfurl in my chest. I cast my eyes heavenward. 'Sorry God,' I murmur.

Hope, Juliet and I hunker down outside as the sun begins to set. I move close to Juliet to generate some warmth. I crave our old threadbare blanket, but it is long gone. A group of boys strolls past. They are laughing and goading each other.

'Oh, look it's the whore's children, Mwe'amabuje,' one sneers.

'Bastard orphans,' another calls.

They are repeating the words of their own parents. People congregate around the entrances of their own shacks, all taking an unwelcome interest in us.

'She slept around, she was a prostitute, good job she's dead now.'

I want to fight, to hit them, to call them devastating names, but Juliet clings to my arm, frightened and upset, so instead I pull her close.

'Maama loved us, that's all that matters.'

We are awake well before dawn. The village is quiet. Stray animals scurry around, dogs sniff for food in the litter, and somewhere a cockerel crows. We watch the small signs of life, waiting for the sun to rise. We huddle closer together to try and keep out the cold, but no one speaks. Mother will be buried today. It is our last day in this house. The landlord has allowed us to stay until Mother's burial, but then we move on, and another poor wretched family will move in. I only hope their life here will be happier than ours.

Hope sniffs, as does Juliet. I hold them tight, kiss the tops of their heads, remember their smell. Ada arrives, looking as though she has not slept much. Her hair is tangled on one side and she holds her arms close to her chest for warmth.

She hugs me. 'Come on, we have to get ready.'

Juliet, Hope and I follow Ada into the house. Jaaja is awake, still moving Maama regularly, an arm, a leg. Her body a dead weight that the old woman struggles with. Beatrice rests on the corner of the sodden mattress. Her eyes are closed but her chest moves erratically. I do not think she is properly sleeping. Seeing her at rest intensifies how frail she

172

has become, her cheek bones protrude from her face, her arms like sticks. She and Mother were best friends in life, and will no doubt soon be reunited in death. I will myself not to think about it.

'We must dress her,' Jaaja instructs.

'In what?' I scan the room but there is nothing, no rags, not even a sheet on the mattress. Nothing fine to send her off to Heaven in. She lies in the same stained, soiled nightdress she wore all those days in hospital.

'We must make her look pretty then.' My heart breaks as Jaaja removes the bright headscarf tied around her hair and the shawl from her own shoulders and wraps her daughter in them. She takes Maama's face in her hands and kisses her forehead before smoothing down her hair, now frizzy in the humidity. She cries silently, the tears glinting on her cheeks as the first rays of sunshine filter through the open door. No Mother should ever have to bury their own child.

We follow Jaaja's lead, all, bar Elizabeth, find something to contribute. Ada covers Maama's bony arms with her own shirt, leaving her in just a plain vest. Juliet finds a small doll from her pocket that we once made from banana fibers and tucks it under her arm. Hope pulls her socks off. She loves those socks, yet she pulls them over Mother's toes. They are too small to cover her whole foot. I have nothing except the simple dress I wear every day. I rip a circle from the hem, where I once ripped a section to mop her up, and quickly plait it. It fits snugly around her wrist and provides a flash of colour, a simple bracelet of goodbye.

'Well then, I think she is ready.' Jaaja slowly rises to her feet, her old bones frailer from a night on a cold, damp floor. Ada places a hand on Beatrice's shoulder to rouse her.

'It's time.'

Some of the villagers gather outside the shack. They seem to know Beatrice and Ada greets them too. Together they pick Maama up and carry her gently into the open. Despite the early hour a small crowd of locals have gathered. Some mutter cruel words, but many look on with sympathy. Women pat their hearts to show their pain. They shake their heads at baby Elizabeth, so young to be without a Mother.

The sky is clouding over once more, threatening rain. I mutter a prayer for it to hold out just a little longer. The streets are already waterlogged. Everything has turned to mud, large puddles seep around every corner. The ditch of open sewage is full and threatening to overflow. The men carry Mother up the street, attempting to avoid the worst of the water but their feet get stuck in the mud every so often. One loses a sandal, the others, who walk barefoot, have feet caked in mud, shoes made from dirt. The going is slow. Jaaja is weeping, Hope too cries and calls out for her Maama. Juliet looks sick, I too feel that way. Ada supports Beatrice, her body too weak to struggle through the water.

At last we reach the ancestral burial site where the clan bury their dead. These are the unmarked graves. It dawns on me that once her grave is filled, I will not know the exact location of it. The men lower her body into a large hole. They try to be gentle but in the last second one slips, and her body falls the last foot or so, landing heavily like a sack of rice. Someone says a few words. My mind flits back to those days at Iris's, lying on that mattress alone, imagining my Mother, wondering where she was, wanting her so badly, imagining her holding me, us playing, laughing together. My life with Mother was never that daydream, but as I stand on the edge of her grave, I am grateful for every day I had with her. I would even endure life with Taata, if it meant I could have my mother back.

The sky rumbles and the rains begin to drip slowly, solemnly from the sky. Jaaja, Ada and some of the men begin throwing handfuls of mud onto her body. The crowds disperse, the spectacle now over. Some approach me as they go, pat me or my sisters on the shoulders, tell us they are sorry. A few women pry pennies into our hands and I pocket them gratefully. Their pennies will feed us for a day or two, but once they are gone, we are alone on the streets of Bwaise.

174

Chapter Thirty-One

Our Grandmother takes us back to her place, but it is only a temporary solution. There is barely enough room for her, and she is elderly and cannot look after us all. The rain is falling hard now, and our clothes are soaked through after our walk through the village. Jaaja takes a large cannister of water and fills a small saucepan which she then places on her stove to warm through, providing us each with a small cup of warming water. Ada has had to return to work and Beatrice to her own children, so Hope, Juliet and I huddle together, Elizabeth on my knee. Hope and Juliet are dazed. They need a guardian, an adult, someone to tell them it will all be fine, that they will be looked after. Instead, they just have me.

'Girls, what can I say, this isn't going to be easy,' Jaaja speaks, 'and what I am going to say next isn't going to help matters.'

Her face has fallen, and she looks weary, her face as tired as I suddenly feel.

'Lela, girls, you have a brother.'

'A brother?'

'Yes.'

'What, how?'

'I know it's hard to take in. Your family is quite extensive, and I need you to understand, your brother, he is not, quite right.'

'Not quite right how?'

'He's a bit…ill. He has never been well. He needs special care which your mother was not able to give him. He has been staying elsewhere. Your mother was furious with me, and made me promise not to interfere, but now she has gone I feel he must be with the rest of the family.'

I nod. Of course, our family needs to stick together, but my head spins slightly and I feel momentarily queasy. What does *elsewhere* mean? My elsewhere was Iris's. Is he in the same kind of purgatory?

'You have had a long day. We can discuss finding him in the morning.'

We are bedded down side by side on mats made from woven grasses, Jaaja kisses each of us, and tells us she loves us.

My stomach tightens as she says it, full of unbearable emotions. Each of us struggles in our own way. Elizabeth snuffles and sneezes as Jaaja attempts to give her the last bottle of the day. Juliet whines for her Maama. Hope too, weeps silently, her shoulders quivering. The girls are quickly asleep. I lie awake, thinking of my brother, of my mother's fury at Jaaja. I wonder if Maama has any other children squirrelled away?

In the morning, Jaaja rummages in her personal belongings to collect enough change to make the journey to find my brother. My sisters are still sleeping, and I feel it is best to make the journey on my own.

'His name is Dembe.' She hands me a rumpled piece of paper with an address scrawled on it. I flag down a boda-boda. How old is my brother? Who is his Father? Why did Mother never mention him? She asked me to find Jaaja, had she hoped she would lead me to him? She should have told me. How could Mother so easily abandon her children? Was it an easy decision? I wonder again if there are more of us out there? The questions circle around my head as I am driven away from Bwaise to an area where the houses look like… houses, rather than tumble-down shacks. I ask the driver to wait while I knock on the door.

The area is better, but this house is tiny, looking like a one room home. There are holes in the walls and the roof and I expect it leaks like ours did. There is no reply.

'Hello, is anyone home?'

I hear no movement from inside so skirt around the back of the compound where I see another small shack, housing a cooking area. The area is covered with banana leaves and a small stove sits in the dirt. The ashes are still smouldering, but where is everyone? I am about to head back towards the boda-boda in defeat when I hear a small scratching noise. I move closer to the second shack, allowing my eyes to adjust to the dark. A boy is squatting in the corner, wearing only a pair of discoloured shorts, his chest bare. His hands cover his face in a pathetic attempt to hide.

'Hello, are you Dembe?'

He fidgets, trying to turn his body away from me.

'I see you,' I say. 'Please can you look at me?'

Still nothing.

'I am your sister, Lela, I have come here to get you.'

He slowly removes his hands from his face, two big brown eyes stare at me. His skin is covered in mud, his palms black with it.

'Can you speak?'

He makes no further movement.

'I have a lift. Please come with me. Our grandmother sent me here. I am to return with you.'

Still he says nothing. I wonder what he could possibly have been through to be this frightened.

'Please, I won't hurt you' I hold an arm out towards him, lowering my voice. There is still no sign of anyone else.

Tentatively, he reaches out for my hand.

'Good,' I encourage, and slowly walk him away from the kitchen. He does not stand straight, his left hand covers the top of his head, and he glances nervously around him. To my relief the driver does not refuse him, allowing us both to climb onto the back of his rusty motorcycle and we swerve back towards Bwaise.

My sisters are awake when we make it back. They play in the mud outside Jaaja's, awaiting my return. Hope calls loudly to our Grandmother as she sees the bike arriving. I feel Dembe trembling behind me, his face buried into my shoulder blade. I signal to Hope to keep the noise down. She understands.

'Dembe, come to your grandmother,' Jaaja calls to him as she approaches, yet he hides further behind me. He is much the same height as I am. He must be close to my age. I wish to speak to him, to ask him, but he does not seem so forthcoming. I am about to take his hand to introduce him to the little ones, but I see to my horror that he is urinating where he stands, right through his shorts. Is he so frightened? I look at Jaaja, she approaches him more cautiously this time, takes him gently by the hand and leads him towards her house.

'Come, we clean you up,' she whispers to him.

Hope looks confused, and asks me a flurry of questions, but she has the sense to keep her voice down. I fear that our long-lost brother is going to make life a lot harder for us, when we have so many issues of our own to contend with.

Beatrice arrives. We run towards her as she moves slowly towards us. She is hunched over.

'Why have you come, Beatrice, when you're in so much pain?' I gently ask her.

'I had to speak to you. Your mother would have wanted me to help.' She edges closer to us and keeps her voice low.

'Jaaja is here?' she enquires.

'Inside, with our brother.'

Her eyes dart to the house. 'Dembe,' she breathes.

'You... knew?'

Beatrice sees my anger.

'You may be angry with a lot of things in life, Lela, and I don't blame you, but it was never my place to tell you about Dembe. It was your mother's.'

I am ashamed. She does not deserve my anger.

'We need to talk about other things,' Beatrice continues. 'You cannot stay here. Your Jaaja is old and does not have the strength, or money to support you all. I'm afraid girls, I do not either. I am sick, and I have my own family to feed. However, Jaaja can manage Juliet and Elizabeth, for now at least. They don't eat much and will make good company. I'm afraid that leaves you two. Hope, I have spoken to the good people at TASO, the people that helped your mother in her final days. They have a place for you at an orphanage not far from here.

'An o-o-orphanage?' She gulps hard as she struggles with the word. 'I am an orphan,' she says, more to herself than either of us. This small fact seems to have escaped her and as she says it, the realisation hits home to me too.

'I don't want to leave you, or Lela, or my sisters. Please take me with you. Don't make me go alone. Can Lela come too?' Her eyes are wide as she clutches hold of my arm.

Beatrice's face is fixed. I wonder if she practiced this face before she left the house, knowing how difficult this may be. I am also wondering why I can't go with Hope.

'I'm afraid Lela is too old. They will not take a twelve-year-old. She will need to settle your sisters, settle your brother somewhere, to settle Jaaja too, but Lela, child, you are reaching an age where you need to do it alone. You need to find some work, somewhere to live, as Ada has done.'

I turn gently to Hope. Her face remains frozen with fear. I hug her to me. 'You will be looked after at the orphanage. The TASO people took very good care of Mother, they will take care of you too. They will feed you, and look after you, and you can learn again, which is what we all want, to be at school. And we will come and see you, understand?'

Hope looks at me in disbelief. 'Ada never comes now.' I sigh, I know it's true.

'Ada has helped with money in the past, and she helps Beatrice too,' Beatrice nods in agreement. 'She has to work and can't visit all the time, but we are a family and we need to do what is best for each other. I will always love you, no matter where I am, or what I am doing. When the time comes, when I am older and can pay my own way, then we can live as a family once more.'

'Family,' she whispers the word, just loud enough for me to hear. I know what she is thinking, and I can't help agreeing with her. Our family is built on secrets and lies, but even so, it's the only one we're ever going to get.

Chapter Thirty-Two

I am alone in Kampala. In my daydreams I work, nothing fancy, just helping in the big houses, sweeping, cooking, that sort of thing, but even this is far out of reach.

I manage the odd job. Some people give me food or small change because they feel sorry for me, but it is never enough to support me for more than a day. My heart aches at the promises I made Hope as I left her, crying alone behind the windows of the orphanage. 'One day we will be together,' I said. It is a far-off dream. Most nights I sleep rough, in doorways, down alleys. There are hundreds of other children in the same boat. If I stick with the kids then I feel a safety in numbers, but without them I'm always afraid. My family don't know where I am. I have comfort knowing the little ones are safe with Jaaja, and that Hope has regular meals and a roof over her head.

Jaaja could not cope with my brother. It was obvious from the start. He had never been taught to use a latrine, he couldn't, or wouldn't speak a word. I was astounded that she had taken him from the only home he had ever known when we were drowning in problems already. Luckily for us, a kind woman in the village took pity on him, took him in to her home, telling us that the 'simple' needed help too. I was envious that Dembe had found shelter so easily. I chided myself for being selfish. At least I had some skills. He is as helpless as a toddler.

It is a Saturday afternoon and I am grateful to have found work in a large house in a wealthy street, my favoured part of town. Often, I am shouted at and told that I am not welcome, but occasionally I am promised a few pennies to work. The streets are wider here, and cleaner, with fewer people, and no open sewage running down the middle. I can smell the flowers growing on the tall trees as I watch the busy men and women coming home from their good jobs. Teachers from the big schools, nurses, shopkeepers. A family is moving to a larger house around the corner. Luckily for me, they needed help. I may be skinny and half-starved, but I have had good training, lugging around toddlers and jerry cans of water.

'You are strong, girl,' the man of the house commented, 'you need work?'

I nodded.

'Help us move and we will pay you well.'

I am now listening closely to his orders. He hands me a large box and I follow them to their new home. As I enter the house I am dumbfounded by the sheer scale of the rooms. Our voices echo in each empty space. The floors are covered with elaborate tiles, the walls washed in bright colours. Everything smells clean. I cannot help but stare. They laugh. I think my awe pleases them.

The morning's work is hard. The sun burns my skin as we cross between the houses, the loads are heavy, and I feel my legs growing shaky as I have not eaten today. Just as I begin to fear that I will not have the energy to complete the task, I hear something wonderful.

A skinny old lady shouts out 'Lunch!' from the old house. Her back is stooped with age. She is wrapped in bright purple cloth, her hair tied away from her face with a matching purple scarf. Her cheekbones jut from her face and she looks as though she would snap if the wind blew too hard.

The family whoop with joy. They have two boys who look very well-fed, yet the eldest complains that he is 'starving.'

'Join us, Lela.' The wife ushers me kindly towards the door. I do not need to be told twice. I follow the family as they climb a narrow flight of stairs to a near empty room. This house may be 'the small, old one' but the size of the kitchen is bigger than our old shack. The elderly lady has created a makeshift table from packing boxes, which are covered with multiple pots full of steaming dishes. I have not seen this much food since the church potluck dinners, and I feel ready to faint with hunger.

'Sit, girl,' says the old woman. She points at one of the scatter cushions placed around the boxes. The chunky boys are already seated, and their father is offering them all bottles of beer.

'For you, Lela?'

'Michael, she is just a child,' his wife says, and she pours me fresh water from a bottle. I have never tasted water so crisp, so cold. On the front of the bottle there is a picture of a mountain, the water must have come straight from the summit. The family begin passing around the dishes of food and I am encouraged to take a spoonful from each. I am careful, not wishing to take too much.

'A bird eats more than that,' the eldest boy remarks.

'Yes, do it properly,' says the younger one. He takes the spoon from my hand and dollops enough food for a whole family onto my plate. I am sure to wake, I think, and find the food gone. I'm not willing to take the risk, so I shovel as much food into my mouth as is humanly possible. The boys smirk and nod in approval. It may be moving day, but no expense has been spared, no detail missed. Each mouthful has a delicate balance of flavours, herbs and spices, meats in rich gravy, fluffy rice and fruity sauces. My stomach fills rapidly, but I don't dare leave anything. I don't know when I will see this much food again.

The meal provides us with the energy we will need to finish the move, but we do not yet continue. The sun is high now and the streets are quieter. The man stretches out on the cool floor and shuts his eyes. The wife and grandmother wash the lunch dishes and add them to the final boxes. I offer to help but they tell me to rest a while. I find an empty room and lie down. The large window is open, and from where I lie, I see the tops of mango trees, small birds hop along narrow branches. The sky is a rich blue. My stomach hurts mildly from being so full. A gentle breeze blows against my skin and I close my eyes. For a moment I wonder if this is what heaven feels like.

When I wake the final boxes are moved to the big house. I can already see the grandeur of the life that will continue here. Large wooden tables and cabinets, chairs with fabric as smooth as silk. It occurs to me it probably is silk. It is all still a mess, but I can already imagine lavish parties. The boys' mother in bespoke gowns, their father in sharp suits. A life I will never know.

'Thank you, Lela, thank you for all your help today, here is what you are owed,' the man called Michael says, and hands over a slim envelope. I know not to open it in front of him, and trust it contains money.

'Thank you, Sir, thank you for your hospitality.'

He nods and I show myself out. When I am clear of the house, I open the envelope discreetly. The white paper is stuffed full of notes. It is more money than I have made all month. I wonder if I have been given the wrong envelope, perhaps this was intended for someone else. Should I return it? My eyes search the streets, but aside from a plump looking dog sniffing the bark of a tree, they are empty. I take the money out and count to be certain. Yes, this is enough to take me home to my family. If this money wasn't intended for me then I am sorry, and I pray to God for forgiveness, but it is time and I am more than ready.

Chapter Thirty-Three

A weak sun is attempting to break through a haze of low hanging cloud as the bus rumbles towards home. I was lucky to find a seat on the packed bus, having waited all night to catch one, there are many standing, shouting to each other. Dogs bark constantly, and the bus is filled with chickens. I feel tired but I know I am so close to home and am too excited to snooze. I am wary too, that if do I nap my envelope will be filched, even though it is carefully tucked out of sight. Kampala has thieves so clever they can *smell* money. So, I amuse myself watching the chickens, clucking and flapping uncontrollably. Every now and then the driver shouts and gestures to lock the birds up, but that only adds to the general hilarity. I get off at the edge of the slums, the alleyways too narrow for the bus to get through. I thank the driver and step into the cool morning air. The thick atmosphere hits me, the stench of too many people packed into a small space, dung, rotting rubbish, human sewage, it feels alien to accept these as the smells of home, yet I do. I long to see my family and am torn as to where to go first, to see how much the little ones have grown at Jaaja's, to visit Ada, Beatrice, or to see if my long-lost brother has flourished at his new home? But it is Hope who draws me. I have never been able to forget her lost, lonely face at the window of the orphanage. The memory still fills me with guilt.

The orphanage dominates the street it stands on. It looks more like a prison than a house for children, with its grey concrete walls, bars on the windows, and a heavy wooden door locked tight as I approach. I knock, unsure it will be heard at all through the thick wood. However, moments later the bolts are opened and a small person peers at me. She looks hardly older than me, but she wears a name badge, and seems to be a person of some importance.

'We are full, please go away.'

I appreciate her mistake. I have not washed in days. My clothes are torn and soiled, and above all, I am an orphan. I quickly correct her.

'No, sorry, I am just here to visit.'

'Well, visiting is on Sunday.'

'Oh,' I must look desperately disappointed as her face softens.

'Look, who are you here to see?'

'Hope. She is my sister.'

'She's outside. Look, I can sneak you in, but you must be fast, understand? Or I will be in trouble.'

'I understand,' I know once I am there I will want to stay, to hold my poor broken sister in my arms, but I will have to be stern. The girl checks that the adults are preoccupied, then steers me through the rooms which make up the orphanage. It is small, considering it houses so many girls. The first room is clearly where the majority of 'life' is undertaken, On the wall is a blackboard and I recognise the forms of the letters I was being taught a lifetime ago. My heart pangs with the want to go back to school. On the opposite wall there are some cooking utensils, pots and pans, and a simple stove with a meal bubbling away. There are no chairs or benches. The girls must sit on the floor. The connecting room is larger in size and appears to be the only bedroom. There must be at least fifty beds, all head to tail in long rows. The beds are small and low to the ground. Aside from a thin mattress they are largely bare. No sheets, or pillows. A couple of them hold a few personal possessions scattered here and there, a book, a doll, not much to signify a happy life. The girl leads me to the yard. It is playtime and all the girls are here. On the far side of the yard are two latrines, side by side and several children queue to wait their turn. Some chase after each other, laughing. I look for Hope's familiar little face. It is not quite the picture I had imagined. These girls have nothing, but they seem happy enough. I scan the perimeters of the yard, looking for a lost little girl, standing forlornly apart from the others, but then I hear her, louder than most, calling and shouting in the old familiar, high-pitched tone. It is the Hope I first saw, the happy child who lived with our old Taata, before the Lout took hold.

'Hope!' I shout over the squeals.

'Lela?' She sees me immediately and runs to hug me. 'Is it really you?'

'Five minutes,' the girl warns. I nod.

'I cannot stay long,' I say to Hope.

'It's not even Sunday, *he* cannot know you are here,' she points to the door.

'Does he treat you badly?'

'Oh no. He's just grumpy. Oh, Lela it's so good to see you,' she beams.

'Hope, you seem happy.'

'Lela, I am happy.' A look crosses her face, I think it is guilt. 'I know, Lela, I know I should be sad, I know Maama is gone, and of course, sometimes I am sad, but mostly I am not. Lela, we don't get a lot to eat, but there is enough, and we eat a little at every meal. No one hurts me here, Lela. Not like Taata used to. Our last Taata, I mean. The girls here are all like me too. We are all the same. Lela, I am learning again, I know how to read now.' I look into her eyes and I feel a huge sense of relief. For months I have struggled with the anguish of leaving her, the weight of it has been bearing down on me daily, but she is doing just fine.

'Are you angry with me, Lela?'

'Oh Hope, of course not. I'm so happy that you are happy. I've worried about you so.' The girl coughs behind me, the signal that my time is up. I pull Hope close to me and hold her tightly, not wanting to let go, but I know I must before we both get into trouble. I promise to visit her again soon.

I head towards Jaaja's house in a party mood. I had dreaded seeing a miserable Hope, and now I know she is just fine, I can return to Jaaja's to play with my sisters and look forward to a warm embrace from my grandmother. Of course, food is tight, but I have some money to contribute now. Perhaps we can have a celebratory meal. I run as Jaaja's house comes into view and look eagerly for the little ones in the yard, but the house seems still, empty.

'Jaaja?' I call.

'Lela?' A little voice answers, tiny, mouse-like from somewhere inside the small abode.

'Hello?' I call again.

A waif-like creature comes into the light. The term 'orphan' personified. She is naked, her arms and legs stick like, her belly rounded, ribs protrude from her skin. The hair on her head has grown long, but it is matted together into small clumps, grey with dirt, like her skin.

'Juliet?'

'Lela, I missed you,' I scoop her into my arms.

'Oh sister, what has happened to you? To Elizabeth? Where is Jaaja?' I am trying to stay calm, to hide the panic in my voice.

'They are sick.' She points but doesn't have much strength to speak further. Is she sick too? I push my way past the sliver that was once a happy, bouncing toddler, now a malnourished ghost of a child. Inside, Jaaja is propping herself up on the table, attempting to cut scraps of vegetables to make a stew, but she is weak and having to stop regularly.

'Jaaja? What is wrong?'

'Oh Lela, you startled me child! How lovely it is to see you, what a surprise!' She raises her arms to hug me briefly, then finds the table once more for support.

'Are you sick?'

'You look thirsty child, are you thirsty? You must be after your journey?'

'Tell me Jaaja? Not AIDS?'

'No, child,' she holds my chin with the tips of two fingers, 'not AIDS. I have lumps Lela, in my breasts, my appetite gone, vomiting, not AIDS but I fear cancer, my dear.' She looks guilty, as though she has let me down.

'Oh, Jaaja, I am so sorry to have left you alone with the little ones. You have known long? Did you try and find me?'

'No, Lela, I will be fine, I have to keep going, the little ones need their food.'

'Where is Elizabeth?' The house is silent, with none of a baby's usual noise. Jaaja's shoulders slump, she hangs her head.

'In the bedroom Lela. She is not well.'

I hurry to the back of the house, a small separate concrete chamber, with three woven mats lining the floor. Elizabeth lies on the floor. Her tiny body has been stripped to just a cloth around her nappy area. The cloth is worryingly dry, and her lips are cracked. Her eyes are closed, but she does not sleep soundly. Her chest heaves with each breath, her throat crackles. Her body is damp with sweat; her skin hot like fire. I hear Jaaja behind me.

'We called a doctor. I paid most of the money I had so he would come. She is desperately ill, Lela. She has measles and malaria together. There was nothing he could do, he said, we just have to wait and see. I would have taken her to the hospital, but I have no money. Or strength,' she adds. Elizabeth's skin is mottled with the measles rash. I run my fingers over it and feel the raised bumps, the cracks, the blemishes. She does not respond to my touch. Frantically, I begin to plan. Elizabeth needs help, but I cannot leave Juliet alone here, she needs a proper meal. I think of Father Silver, but the church is too far in the opposite direction from Jaaja's. I need somewhere on route to hospital. I begin throwing their few belongings into a bag, kiss Jaaja and tell her I will take Juliet to Beatrice, and then Elizabeth to hospital. She looks relieved, she needs rest.

We make the brief journey to Beatrice's. I am alive with anxiety, as Elizabeth's breath is shallower, her body is limp in my arms. Her limbs hang heavily to the side. Every few minutes she holds her breath for a moment, then the rasp comes back.

'Keep breathing, little girl.' I whisper in her ear, still, no response.

As we get to Beatrice's, I bang urgently on the door of the tiny shack, fearful she may be out, but I hear signs of life in the single room behind the door. I bang again. At last Beatrice opens the door, and we both gasp as she does so. She is just a shadow of the person I once knew. She is in the darkest phase of AIDS. Now I see that Maama's fate will soon be hers. She is horrified at the sorry little creatures I have brought to her doorstep. Skin, bones, disease, decay.

'What happened?' Beatrice's voice is pitched with horror.

'I cannot stop, Beatrice, Elizabeth needs the hospital.' She nods. 'I need you to look after Juliet.'

She attempts to pick her up.

Beatrice is in no better state than Jaaja, but there is no time to argue. I kiss my sister on her matted head and carry Elizabeth, no heavier than a rag doll, to the boda-boda.

I hold my own breath until the familiar, frightful sight of Mulago hospital comes into view. I had hoped never to see it again.

I pay the driver, who looks disappointed with what I offer him, but I need to keep what is left to convince the nurses to help my sister. In this place, money talks. Elizabeth's tiny body is so light in my arms now, I may as well be carrying a bundle of cloth. Her skin is tormented with fever, and her limbs jerk. I sprint up the walkway, past a crowd of men arguing at the entrance.

'Help,' I shout as soon as I enter the building, my call unheard. I did not think it possible, but the hordes are thicker today than when we were first here with Maama. The nurses herd people into long lines. Even the rich must wait today. My mind races, remembering Harry Talisman, the doctor that helped us all those months ago. To my dismay I remember it is Thursday, his day for working in the slum.

'Help me, my baby, my sister, she needs help! Is Dr Talisman here? He is our doctor; he knows what to do.' A nurse jostles me towards a line, the longest, without saying a word. There are two hundred people in this queue alone.

'She has no time,' I plead. I wave my pitiful wad of cash under her nose. She looks at it in disgust.

'Everyone must wait, child. Do not argue with me.' She moves on to the next sorry individual to walk through the doors.

I sing softly into Elizabeth's ear. I make the words up, plucking them from the air. She does not cry. I long to hear a murmur, but she is silent bar the rattle which comes with each moth breath. Still I sing, if anything to make myself feel better. Her breathing is shallower now, her fight is fading. My own tears fall, but I bury my face close to my sister and keep humming tunefully. If my voice sounds joyful enough, she may come back to me. 'Please stay here, sweet girl, stay with me, I shall not leave you again, I promise, stay with me.' My pleading is in vain. Her eyelids flicker once, and after a pitiful cough I know she is gone. I feel her chest, shake her slightly, but there is nothing. Her body is just bones, the life in it extinguished.

190

No one notices us. No one sees two orphan girls, a big one, cradling her infant sister in a crowded room. Grown men shout loudly, demanding treatment. Doctors are too overworked to notice a dying child. We are invisible. My throat is so tight I can hardly breathe. I slip silently from our place in the queue. The woman behind us steps forward, filling the space and smothering our shadows as though they were never cast. I clutch Elizabeth's minuscule frame close to my own, not wanting to jolt her as I wrestle for the exit, even though she is far beyond pain now. I am small enough to skim past neighbouring arms, over abandoned bags, between unfamiliar legs. Then we are back in the open air, the pollution of Kampala filling my lungs. I hold my chin up high, though blinded by prickling tears. I follow the light which filters through them. The crowd of men grows quiet as we pass.

'Oh child,' one mutters.

'Peace be with you,' says another.

They are the first to recognise a grief-stricken child cradling her lifeless infant sister.

Chapter Thirty-Four

The grief surges through me like poison. But it is a sickness which cannot be quelled. It haunts me in my dreams, her face returns to me, her tiny hands, her faint, rattled breath. In my waking hours my ears scour the air for her voice, the gurgles which amused us so, the baby cries which kept us awake at night. To think we used to complain. My only reassurance? That Mother was not here to bear this burden. She is long gone, but it is her words that keep me awake at night.

'Lela, this is your fault.' 'Lela, how could you let my baby die?' 'Lela, you should have come home sooner.'

This grief burns through my soul. We had months to prepare for Maama's death. Elizabeth's passing is such a sudden shock. Her fate is a common one in the slums. A child's life brought to a sudden end by a wholly preventable illness, a fear which afflicts the natives daily. Ripe sewage surrounds their homes, their children are tormented with diarrhoea, malaria, malnutrition, dehydration. They could rise tomorrow only to find themselves burying one of their own by sunset. No one is better off than anyone else, and if they believe they are, fate will strike them next.

I returned to Beatrice's with my lifeless bundle in my arms. Neighbours quickly gathered round me. Some began wailing and patting their hearts with their hands. Others slunk away, as if I was carrying a ghost to her doorstep. My legs were moving, miraculously propelled in the right direction. I was close to collapse when some man took Elizabeth from me. A hefty woman of considerable age helped me from the floor. Her face was as wrinkled as a road map from smiling, though she was not smiling that day. I watched the stranger carrying my infant sister. He was huge, with a scarred face and a nose that had been broken several times. I would have been terrified of meeting him in a darkened street, but he trembled as he looked down on Elizabeth.

Inside, the kids were silent, huddled together in a corner. They knew not to shout or run around. I was handed some lukewarm water to drink. I sipped at it carefully. Beatrice moved slowly around the room, assailed by illness, dragged down by constant worry, disease, impending death and grief for the tiny child lying dead on her table. She could not look at Elizabeth. Everyone seemed to know their role. The elderly lady poured more fresh water from the large cannister into a metal bowl. She ripped a strip of fabric from the hem of her skirt. No wonder, as Beatrice was too ill to keep her house or her children clean.

The lady washed Elizabeth's tiny body and dried her matted hair. Then the scary looking stranger took over. Silent tears were pouring down his face, and my throat closed over again. He laid a small hessian sack beside her body and carefully picked her up. In his hands Elizabeth looked even smaller, her bones scrawny, her body unfed. My stomach churned with guilt. Putting the baby in the bag was too much for him. He sobbed like a child. At last, Beatrice gently took my sister from him. In her arms, Beatrice finally looked at her.

'I'm sorry little girl, I am so, so sorry.' It was not grief that had stopped her from looking at Elizabeth. It was guilt. I understood perfectly. Beatrice kissed my sister's cold head, holding back her own tears, and gently slid her away from sight into the hessian sack. A coffin was laughably out of reach. My sister would be buried in nothing better than a bag they put rice in. Rice which we could not afford.

Beatrice cuddles her close, and keens as she rocks her from side to side. The time had come. None of us wanted to wait twenty-four hours for people to say their goodbyes. The gentle giant had pulled himself together, and he determinedly took the sack from Beatrice. He was the only one who could carry Elizabeth. Everyone else was too sick, too old or too small. I was in too much shock.

He picked her up with both hands and placed her gently against his shoulder. I pictured Maama holding Elizabeth this way, to burp her, as a newborn. My eyes pricked at the memory. We followed him out of the house, supporting each other and holding the hands of the children. Somewhere, Ada was scrubbing floors and tending to rich people, believing her family to be safe. Hope was happily playing with her friends in the orphanage, practicing her alphabet. Both blissfully unaware of the hammer blow to come.

We did not attract the usual attention given to a funeral procession. We were just a group of sorry looking misfits carrying a hessian sack down a busy street. Beatrice's neighbours nodded their respects, bowed their heads, whispered words or prayers, but further on we were ignored, and I was grateful for that.

We had to take Elizabeth's lifeless body to Jaaja's, there was nowhere else for her to go. There was no space for her in an ancestral graveyard.

I could see the stooped, frail silhouette of my grandmother leaning against her front door. How long had she been waiting there? As she saw us, her frail, high pitched cry tore through the street.

We filed through Jaaja's small dwelling and out of the rear door into the compact yard. It wasn't much, but it was somewhere a little girl could be buried without wild dogs digging her up. The gentle giant dug hard, but the ground was rocky, it took time. Jaaja cried herself into silence, Beatrice dozed exhausted in one corner, her children by her side. Some of Jaaja's neighbours brought food for the party to eat. The old woman busied herself arranging it for us.

At last with the moon high above our heads the hole was deep enough to lay a body to rest. Jaaja asked for help lifting the sack. If anyone was to place the child in that hole, she felt it was her duty to do so. The hole was deep, and Jaaja too weak to reach the bottom. Elizabeth's little body fell the last foot, creating a thud as it hit the ground. That sound will stay with me always, as will the cruel irony of her dying on a Thursday in the hospital, when Harry Talisman was in the slums.

'One day we shall meet again, little Elizabeth, I have read so in the Bible. We shall meet in a paradise where we shall not feel hunger, where we will not be beaten or abused, where we will be loved. In a place where disease will not rip families apart. You will play, and we shall shout and laugh. You will know what happiness feels like. Be at rest, my sister, this world did not deserve you. When I wake in the morning, I will think of you first and when I am ready to sleep, I will think of you last. Your face will not grow old, but your memory will grow old with me.'

Part Two

A Hope of Adolescence

Chapter Thirty-Five

Eighteen months later, I hold a long piece of striped fabric in my left hand. It is called a tie. I see my reflection as I attempt to thread it through my collar, but the lesson I had yesterday is already forgotten. I will have to ask Ann to show me again. The face that stares back at me is nothing like the tattered, grief-stricken girl who sat in the dirt beside her sister's grave.

'Victoria Academy,' I breathe, barely daring to utter the words, in case this is a dream and speaking the name will wrench me out of the euphoric state that I am in.

My crisp white shirt is buttoned to the throat, cornflower blue skirt meeting the knees, pressed blazer with the Victoria Academy emblem beaming like a lit beacon from the breast pocket.

Victoria Academy is a prestigious boarding school some miles into the rich Kampala, far from Bwaise, from the sewage, the smell, but away from my family too. I used to watch the television advert through the window of a small shop in the centre of the city as I searched for work, between orphanages, between homes, desperate for someone to take me in. I watched clips of the girls and boys, clean, well dressed, happy. They were learning, leaning over solid wood desks, pens in hand, writing in notebooks with lined pages. They were clothed in white, playing sports like football and others I don't even recognise. I saw rows of beds, but only a few to a room, each one made with fresh white bedding, turned down in one corner. I saw the name flash at the end of the commercial: Victoria Academy School. It seemed like Heaven to me, like an unreachable dream yet here I am. God has answered my prayers, and is to take me away from my troubles, and let me be a child again.

As if on cue, behind me a small knock turns my attention.

'Come in,' I say gently. The door creaks open and Ann stands behind me.

'Oh Lela, look at you.' she gasps at the sight of me, a look of pride, this dear friend of mine just as happy as I am.

'Oh Ann,' I step away from my reflection to approach the lady I now class as family.

'Come,' she signals for me to hand over the tie. 'You do it like this.' She turns my body towards the mirror so I can see how she does it. She performs a series of loops, like a dance with her hands, and suddenly the tie is knotted smartly over the button of my collar.

'How did you-?'

'Don't worry, you'll get the hang of it soon enough,' Ann smiles at me and I hug her.

Ann took me in when she found me sleeping in a church. She persuaded the priest to give me a place at school. She told me he wanted to send me to a nunnery as my grades were terrible. Ann let me stay with her. She had no money to school me, but she fed and cared for me and three other children, until finally she could no longer keep us.

In her hand are my admission papers. She places them on top of the small suitcase I shall be taking to school with me. It is a modest case, but I do not have much. A clean uniform, my schoolbooks, some night wear, all purchased by Amanda, my other saviour.

I had met Amanda by attending a Christian crusade some miles from Ann's home. She had been with a friend, a woman so elegant I could barely keep my eyes off her. Her hair was swept off her neck, large sunglasses shadowed her eyes, and her clothes were soft, pure white linen. She looked like a movie star. I had wanted so badly to speak to her, but when I got close - beautiful though she was - she had backed away as if I had fleas. Alarmed to have a street child grasp at her hand without warning, I'm sure. But It was Amanda who approached me, spoke to me - asked me my name.

'Oh Amanda.' Her friend had said dismissively. 'You and your ragamuffins.' Amanda had given me money for the bus and invited me to meet her the following day at Nandos, a fine cafe I had often passed, but had never dreamed of entering.

I arrived early. I looked terribly out of place amongst the swanky throngs of European faces. I was wearing an old summer dress Ann had given me. The waitress squinted at me.

'You girl, not looking for trouble, are you?'

'No madam, I am here to meet someone.'

'Who?'

In panic at the thought of being thrown to the streets, I forgot her name, but then I heard her voice.

'Le-le!' She waved at me over the heads of busy customers.

'Lela.' I corrected her but smiled in relief.

The waitress sourly showed us to a table with two seats. Amanda offered me an ice cream.

'What is ice cream?'

'Ice cream? Oh Lela,' for a moment I thought she would laugh at me, but she took my hand instead. 'I'm sure you'll like it.' When the ice-cream arrived it certainly was the most beautiful food I had ever seen. Served in a glass longer than my face, balls of colour piled one on top of the other. A stick of chocolate perched on top and a million coloured strands sprinkled all over.

'Eat up then, before it melts.'

'Melts?' I smiled and she laughed, though without intent.

The sensation took me by surprise. It was so cold; unlike anything I had had before. It made my teeth hurt, and my head developed a sharp pain.

She laughed. 'You just had a brain freeze. You've got to take it easy.'

I took a smaller mouthful, wary next time. 'Mmm. It's delicious,' I said.

'What do you have, tea?'

'Coffee. You want to try?'

She passed me her cup full of a deep brown liquid. It smelt rich, luxurious. It looked like the tea Jaaja had given me. I took a sip, then made a face.

'Do you like tea?' I nodded and soon the waitress arrived again with a dinky teapot and cup just for me.

I found myself telling Amanda all about Maama's AIDS and about Elizabeth. She was such a good listener that I even managed to tell her about Iris, and about Mussa. She held my hand whenever my story pained me and by the end, she was willing to do what she could to help me. It was she who gave me the chance to attend the school of my dreams.

I am soon in an air-conditioned car with Ann, on my way to Victoria Academy School, away from yet another place I have briefly considered home. I was sad to say goodbye to the other children she was looking after and pray that they find happy homes now she no longer has the money to keep them. She will do her best for them, of that I'm sure. I'm leaving my siblings once again with Beatrice and Jaaja, both hanging on by a thread. Nonetheless, I am excited, and can't help but feel happy. Outside lush trees and green grass flash between stately houses, with long curving drives. We are heading towards Lubiri and Kabaka's Palace and I stare open-mouthed at the sheer luxury of the place. We have left poverty behind. The people here live in beautiful homes. They have cushy jobs working for the government, and never have to worry about where their next meal is coming from.

There are many new students, like me, some looking lost, others excited and happy. The old students greet each other with warm embraces. As it is a boarding school, it reassures me to see how they welcome each other. Ann asks if I am nervous as we step from the car, but I am not. I am dressed the same way as everyone else. I already feel like I belong. Amanda bought me the new case; my shoes are smart. I do not look different. I do not look poor.

Ann accompanies me to the front office. A girl, younger than I, is crying as she holds tightly to her mother's hand. 'Please do not leave me, Mama, let me stay with you and Father.' Her mother, a regal looking woman dressed in an ivory coloured skirt suit shuffles on her high heels, embarrassed. 'Marie, we have spoken of this, many times. We have to work, to travel. This is the best place for you.' The girl nods sadly, unconvinced. A tall, white man with a greying beard approaches our group carrying a battered looking clipboard. Mr. Van Bjorn, one of the school's founders.

'Welcome! Let me take your names, then you'll have to say goodbye to your parents.' Marie edges even closer to her mother. 'I'll show you to your dormitories.'

I am sad to see Ann go, but I can't think of anywhere else I would rather be.

Mr. Van Bjorn waits patiently as Marie clings to her exasperated mother, who is prizing herself away.

'I am new too,' I say. 'Would you like to be my friend?' She is so small, and I feel for her.

She smiles tightly, and hesitantly waves to her mother. Mr. Van Bjorn nods his approval and leads us back through the busy playground, where cars are still arriving, and girls scream at each other in joy. The idea of having friends that scream with excitement when they see me is thrilling. We cross the yard, past a long, grand-looking building, to smaller cabins on the edge of the grounds.

'The large hall is for worship, gatherings and performances,' Mr. Van Bjorn explains. 'There are separate classes for lessons. Unlike many schools in Uganda, we separate our year groups and you will move to various classes throughout the day. For example, we have rooms dedicated to science with all the required equipment. You'll also find the food hall in the main building where all meals are served.'

Three meals a day, free, cooked by someone else. The luxury of it!

'Over here,' he continues. 'are our dormitories. Girls are on this side and boys over there. There will be no mixing of girls and boys in the dormitories at any time. There are three dorms on the girl's side, one for the younger girls, one for the middle years, and the older girls get the biggest one at the top there.'

They are all immaculate. Clean walls with no cracks, and sparkling windows with fine cotton curtains which sway in a fresh breeze.

'Lela and Marie, you are in here, your beds are marked with your names. Make yourselves comfortable. You'll have an hour to settle in before the whole school meets in the main hall. Any questions? Oh, I nearly forgot – latrines and the shower block are over there.' He leads the others away.

Still holding Marie's hand, we show ourselves in. The dorm is still empty, and I am grateful for some time to settle in before the other girls arrive. Within the cabin are bunk beds, three top to tail on one side and another two on the opposite side of the room. There are also two large chests of drawers with five drawers each. My name is clearly printed by hand on one of the bottom drawers, and on the top bunk of the bed closest to the door, with Marie directly below me.

'Well, this is lovely,' I smile.

Marie shrugs. She is probably used to a grander, more private bedroom, but she doesn't complain, simply slumps on the end of her bed. As I unpack my few belongings into the drawer, I see a group of girls heading towards the dorm with their cases. I straighten my uniform and wait protectively close to Marie, ready to greet my next family.

Chapter Thirty-Six

Victoria Academy is a paradise for me. I go to bed every evening with a full belly and sleep more soundly than I ever have. I sleep in a room with girls just like me, who are my friends, and do not treat me like a servant. The teachers see me as a student, not an imbecile. I'm safe from hunger, far away from abusers, criminals, the horror of AIDS. Whilst I'm happy, my dreams are constantly haunted by the family I have left behind. My sisters, my sick grandmother. I tell myself that only education can get me a job good enough to support them, that we'll be together again one day. I pray it is part of God's grand plan.

I throw myself into my studies. I want to do my sponsors proud. They believe in me and so I, in turn, believe that I can become something great. I will work hard to become a somebody, to make money, to save my sisters from the life of poverty they were born into. I work harder and later than the other girls. Often, when they are playing, I am perched on my bed, practicing my reading, or maths. The girls tease me, call me a brain box, but they are not nasty and are happy to help me when I get stuck. I am so far behind the others, as for so many years eating has trumped education.

I love the drama classes. I can be both who I truly am, and who I would like to be. On stage I feel fully free. I can be strong, I can be vulnerable, I can be funny! I can confront the villains, and can demonstrate my pain, instead of hiding it deep inside me. When I cry onstage it is real. I get a chance to cry for all I have lost.

'Lela, you are good,' says Mrs. Doomer, the tiny drama teacher in her booming voice. I am chosen for the end-of-year show.

The show comes quickly. I peek through the curtain, quelling my fluttering stomach, wishing my mother and sisters were there to see me. Amanda is in the audience, my wonderful sponsor who has given me the keys to this glorious castle. I see her chatting to another couple. Being white, they stand out in a sea of black Ugandans.

The lights go down and a spotlight points directly at the thick, double lined curtains. Marie has been drafted in as stagehand and raises the curtain. She isn't good at organising the props and her timing is off, and Mrs. Doomer is shooting her a look. Marie hands me the microphone.

'Nervous?' she asks, but before I have time to reply I am thrown into the spotlight.

I am terrified of disgracing myself and shaming my amazing sponsor, Amanda. I feel a line of sweat trickle from my tightly braided hair down the side of my scalp. I scratch at it and try to focus as I await my cue.

Three of my dorm friends end a trio to a burst of applause. I'm so proud. I had helped them practice every night. Mrs. Doomer gives a thumbs up from behind the wings. Then she nods at me. I have survived so much; I can do this too. I step onto the stage, first footstep hesitant, but I soon find my confidence. The spotlight blinds me to the audience, but I feel all those eyes upon me. My introduction comes from an ancient piano and I draw my breath and sing. My voice soars high, confident, my arms spread in character. For three minutes I am not Lela, Ugandan girl from the slums. I am still an orphan, but I'm a little cheeky one from New York, singing my heart out about Tomorrow. I hold the final top note in triumph, then for a split second there is silence before the audience erupts with applause. I take a huge bow and depart.

'Lela, you were amazing,' Marie hugs me and grabs the microphone, dropping a pile of hair ribbons as she does so. I beam. She does not dole out compliments easily.

When the show is over, I change out of my 'Annie' costume, eager to see Amanda. Marie dawdles as she gathers up the props.

'Not meeting your Maama?' I ask.

'She decided not to come. I'm glad I didn't sing or act now. They wouldn't have been here to watch me anyway.'

'Oh, Marie.' I hug her. She is tense in my arms, stiff like a tree trunk.

'I know what it's like not to have your family close by,' I offer.

'I know, Lela,' she softens. 'I know your mother died.'

'How do you know?' I had kept my family's sorry story to myself.

'I saw it on your records, that first morning. It said 'orphan' on the clipboard.'

Before I betray how I feel about her knowing this about me, she says: 'Lela, don't you see, if your mother was alive, she would be here, clapping, standing in ovation, just like everybody else tonight. She would have wanted to see her daughter perform. My mother? She couldn't care less.' She drops her box of props and runs out.

'Marie!' I call out but she has gone.

I have a sudden revelation. If my mother was alive, she would not be here, and neither would I, we would still be slumming it. Victoria Academy would be an elaborate dream, a make-believe scenario for rare play time fun. I have Victoria Academy only because my mother is dead. I would trade it all to have my mother back. I don't have time to think further, as Amanda is waiting for me with her friends and I am keen to make a good impression.

'Lela!' Amanda waves as she catches me peeking from behind the curtain. I smile and stretch out my arm for a handshake, as I've been taught. She pulls me closer and hugs me instead. It feels good.

She takes my hand. 'I want to introduce you to my friends. This is Mr. and Mrs. Webb.'

I offer my hand again, to both.

'It's so lovely to meet you at last,' says Mrs. Webb as she shakes my hand. She rests her other hand on our closed fists.

'At last?' I enquire.

'Lela, come and sit with us. How are you getting on here?' She continues.

'Oh, I love it, I really do, it's wonderful,' I enthuse, a little over-dramatically. I am worried they are here to remove me.

'It's ok, Lela. We can all see you're doing well here,' smiles Mrs. Webb. She has a kind smile. I wonder why she is here. Her brown hair falls in front of her wide rimmed glasses and she removes them to polish them on the hem of her pale pink skirt.

'Lela,' says Amanda, 'remember when we first met, I said I couldn't afford to sponsor you? Well, that is still true, yet here you are, thanks to the Webbs. They work alongside me at the Mission. After I met you, I spoke to the other members. The Webbs wanted to help. At first anonymously, but when I told them how well you were doing, they wanted to come and meet you themselves.'

I didn't know how to thank people who had never met me, had no association with me whatsoever, yet who had given me a piece of my childhood back, a chance to be young again, a chance for a future which did not feature hunger or abuse.

'I am so grateful to you; I don't know what to say.'

'There is nothing to say, child, we are happy to help, that has always been our calling,' says Mr. Webb. He is tall, taller than most in the room, his hair greying and balding on top. His skin is very white, I cannot help but stare, like most of the others do.

'I have worked so hard on my studies. I hope you are happy and want me to stay?' I am jabbering, but my nerves have taken over.

'Lela, we are very pleased with you, and we have been talking. We would really like you to join us for the holidays.'

'The- the holidays?' I stammer.

'We live fairly close by, just on the edge of Kampala. We have a nice house and garden, nothing special, but we can make you comfortable.'

'Live with you, for the whole holiday, like a family?' For a moment I wonder if I have overstepped the mark, but the Webbs smile at each other.

'Yes, Lela. Like a family.'

I hug them, I am so relieved. I had not known how I was to get home for the holidays, and I had been afraid to ask. All the other girls had talked excitedly about their plans. One wanted to get back to her pets, another chattered about the local swimming hole near Lake Victoria, where she could swim with her brothers. Marie, I knew, was to spend the holiday alone with the family housekeeper as her parents were in Europe. I longed to go home to see my sisters, to see how Jaaja and Beatrice were holding up. I simply didn't have the means to get home. I did not feel it was my place to ask Amanda for money to travel home. I also had wondered how my family would feel if I turned up so well, healthy, full of food and dressed in clean, crisp clothes, with nothing to offer them. I had been paralysed by awkwardness, wondering if I would be the only child to stay at school while everyone else was away.

Now though, I could pack my case and head off on a real holiday. I would try to see my family. I hope they know how much I love them. I write regular letters home. Beatrice could read, and I wanted the others to know I was thinking of them, even if I couldn't send what they really needed: money. God has answered all the prayers I have made for myself. I can only hope he helps my family one day too.

Chapter Thirty-Seven

I am seated in the back seat of Mr. Webb's car, waving madly as my friends run alongside, cheering and calling my name. Mrs. Webb smiles at her husband.

'How far is your house? What is your home like?' I try and remember my manners. So many questions could be considered rude. I do not know the etiquette of white people. Is it rude to ask about their house?

'It's a modest house, but it's comfortable. We both hope it will feel like home to you.' I sit on my hands to stop myself fidgeting. The world whizzes by outside the window. Men, two or three at a time pass on overcrowded motorcycles, dirty pick-up trucks filled with children and animals cut in front of us. Mr. Webb quietly concentrates on the crazy Kampala roads. I am not surprised. His car is very shiny. It is silver and gleams under the hot sun. I have never seen a car so well kept, not a scratch on it. The interior has a leathery, inviting smell, and the black seats are cool against my skin.

Eventually the roads begin to calm, and we drive past lush green palm trees, the leaves rippling gently in the breeze. The landscape changes to well-kept gardens dotted with the odd group of pretty villas. After what seems like an age the car begins to slow.

'In a moment, dear, we will be home.' I sit as far forward as my seatbelt will allow as Mr. Webb slowly maneuvers the vehicle towards a gate. A young man in a security uniform gives him a wave and the gate to the compound opens automatically, as if by magic. The compound is very different to anything I am used to. The external walls are whitewashed to perfection, surrounding four spacious houses, separated by large swathes of lawn. The grass is a vivid green and shimmers in the sunshine. I hear a hissing noise and I watch, amused, as water sprays itself across the lawn. Beautiful jackfruit trees line the driveway and as we stop, I am overwhelmed by the scent of jasmine. I am speechless. Mr. Webb takes my hand and helps me from the car.

'This is us!' Mrs. Webb exclaims as she directs me towards the solid, dark wooden front door almost hidden under boughs of pink bougainvillea. Like most houses in Uganda, it is set over one floor, but there, the similarity ends. Their entrance hall is bigger than our old shack. Mrs. Webb leads me on a 'guided tour.' Each room seems more wonderful than the last. Beautiful cream sofas adorn the cool living room, a fan turns above our heads, little tables dotted around the walls, covered in delicate frames holding the faces of many smiling children, black and white. I wonder if they have any children of their own, but I'm afraid to ask. The kitchen is so spotless I do not believe anyone has ever eaten in here. The counter tops are so gleaming that they show my reflection.

'Now Lela, dinner will be around seven,' says Mrs. Webb, 'but if you are hungry beforehand, please help yourself to a snack. You're welcome to eat anything you like.'

I smile politely, my eyes scanning the counters. There is no sign of actual food in this vast kitchen.

'Come,' Mr. Webb directs me to a tall, white, rectangular box in the corner. 'This is our fridge.'

He opens it to reveal a huge array of food. All for just for one small family; shelves of meat, vegetables, mysterious things in little glass pots. Enough food to feed my own family for a month.

'There are crisps and biscuits in this cupboard. We weren't sure what you like.' She shows me another place jam-packed with food, everything wrapped in neat little colourful packets.

'I like to eat everything!' I exclaim, and they laugh. My thoughts flit back to my sisters. How I would love to bring them some of this food.

'Anyway, you must be tired after the car journey. Shall I take you to your room?'

'I get my own room?'

'Well, of course!' He doesn't know I have never had a space of my own.

They take me down a small passageway off the main hall and open the whitewashed door at the end.

I gasp, I can't help it. My room looks like something out of a magazine. So much white. Everything is crisp. The enormous bed is covered in immaculate sheets, and the pillows are soft and fat.

'Do you like it?'

'Wow, yes, thank you, thank you so much! Everything is so white!'

'Ha-ha, well yes, we have a very reliable washing machine.'

'What is a washing machine?'

'Ha-ha, we'll leave you to unpack. Make yourself at home, and see you for dinner, dear.'

I open my suitcase and hang my things in the whitewashed wardrobe and pretty chest of drawers. There is a small dark bookshelf in the corner. I pick up a book and skim the pages. The text is complex, too advanced for me yet. I pick up a small Bible. This is more to my liking. I sit myself on the corner of the bed intending to read it, but I am comfortable so quickly, and the mattress feels as if it were made of a million feathers. I am soon asleep.

'Lela, Lela dear? Dinner's ready,' Mrs. Webb is gently shaking me, her soft hair framing her kind face. Dinner smells delicious, of fragrant spices which are unfamiliar to me. Dusk is now falling, and the hallway lights are on, six of them just for this little space. In the main hall, the light is even more radiant, a central pendant hanging low with tiny jewelled crystals reflecting onto the marble flooring. I finger the hem of my uniform nervously. Perhaps I should have dressed for dinner.

'Don't worry, its only us for dinner tonight,' says Mrs. Webb.

Mr. Webb is already at the dining table, and he rises slightly as Mrs. Webb directs me to my seat. The table is long, but only three places are laid at one end. Mr. Webb sits at the head and Mrs. Webb and I at either side of him. Mrs. Webb returns from the kitchen with a whole roasted chicken.

'Roast chicken, I hope you don't mind, it's one of my favourites.'

I have always been grateful for food of any kind, but this is a meal I shall always remember. It is cooked simply, but the meat is perfectly tender and juicy, the skin seasoned with smalls grains of green herbs which are not native to Uganda.

My plate is clean in no time.

'You didn't mind that too much, Lela?' Mr. Webb enquires. I realise he is poking gentle fun at me. I laugh and accept a second helping.

'I'm sorry,' I smile.

'Don't be,' Mrs. Webb smiles, 'It's a huge compliment to the chef.'

'Tomorrow we were thinking of taking you swimming at the country club, what do you think?'

'Sounds amazing!' I say. I have never swum before in my life, but why let that spoil our evening?

Chapter Thirty-Eight

The days pass in a blur of laughter, fun, and the feeling of belonging. I feel part of a real, conventional, loving family. But my thoughts stray constantly to my sisters, and their two sick and rickety old guardians. The Webbs allow me a certain amount of freedom to come and go as I please. This part of Kampala is safe, so I roam and explore when they were tied up with work. Mrs. Webb hands me money and tells me to go and enjoy myself.

On the first day I held those coins tightly in the palm of my hand as I strolled down a dusty track, past food markets and restaurants, the dust flying up from my smart new sandals. I wanted to get the coins to my sisters. After giving me a little money each day, I now have enough to take it to my sisters myself. I want to tell the Webbs, but I worry that it would seem ungrateful for me to want to go back to my old life. I decide to say nothing. We usually spent the mornings together, then they work in the afternoon until dinner time. If I can catch a bus to Bwaise and back I will be home well before dinner.

'You don't mind being by yourself in the afternoons do you, dear?' Mrs. Webb enquires at lunch.

I assure her I'm quite happy.

'Well if you're sure, dear. I have a few errands to run and then we must meet with our minister to discuss our sponsorships but then I will be home to make dinner. Would you like to help? I was thinking of making *Stamppot*. It's a traditional Dutch dish that my mother used to make, I thought it might be fun to do it together.'

'That sounds lovely,' I smile.

As soon as they are gone, I hurry to the bus stop, glancing quickly at the watch the Webbs had given me along with all my new clothes. I have only just learned to tell the time. Mr. and Mrs. Webb's compound is further from the main bus route than I expected, so I run. The sun burns brightly in the cloudless sky. I run in the shade of the surrounding fruit trees but still, I am sweating by the time I reach the stop. A large woman with a baby strapped to her chest is fanning herself with a palm leaf.

215

'You missed it, child, same as me. He needed changing, and the driver wouldn't wait. Always missing something these days is me.'

'How long till the next?' I glance nervously at my watch once more.

'Ha, this is Uganda, child, did you just drop from the sky?'

I flop down in the dust, copying the fanning motion with my hand. It only makes me hotter. She's right. This *is* Uganda. If a timetable existed, it would tell me that the bus *should* be along in ten minutes. But it will be along when it is along, in fifteen minutes if there are chickens in the road, twenty minutes if the driver stopped for the latrine, thirty minutes if it is overcrowded and the suspension doesn't hold up. Never if it hits one of the thousands of kamikaze bikers. On this occasion I am in luck, and the bus trundles towards us after only twenty minutes, surrounded by a cloud of dust. The last of the rains have long gone. I cough as I climb onboard, offering the driver the exact change for a return journey. There is nowhere for me to sit, but I do not mind. I am longing to see them all, but my stomach is heavy with anxiety at what I will find.

The bus finally draws up close to Bwaise. The stench hits me more viciously than ever before and I steady myself against a nearby wall. I should have brought water with me. I try to close my nose off to the smell of the ever-flowing stagnant open sewage. I constantly brush flies off my skin. I tread carefully, thinking Mrs. Webb would not be happy if I stain my five-day-old sandals with excrement. I am so conspicuous in my clean clothes and smart sandals. I once played in these slums, unconcerned with the waste and the smell and now my watch, my pretty shoes, and clean, crisp clothes (that washing machine really does work) mark me for the outsider I have become. I am relieved when Beatrice's house comes into view.

The door to her house is wide open. Wet clothes are draped over one of her chairs, drying in the sunshine, and I take this to be good sign.

'Hello?' I call as I near.

'Lela?' As my eyes adjust to the dim light inside her shack, I see Beatrice, slumped, exhausted, on a chair, a rag draped on her sweaty forehead. She is so thin that her cheek bones protrude from her sallow skin. She was always beautiful, admired for her full breasts and curvy hips but they are long gone. I hug her. It is like embracing the skeleton of a bird.

'Where are the kids?' I ask, trying not to panic.

'They're playing in the street. They are ok.'

'All of them?'

'All except Dembe, he is with your Jaaja.'

'Is he well?'

'As well as he always was, but still withdrawn, still won't speak. Your Jaaja tries, but he does very little.' I nod, remembering how in this life it is sometimes easier just to withdraw.

'I am so sorry, Beatrice, that I haven't come sooner, that I didn't send money, have you had food?' Her gaunt appearance shocks me.

'Oh Lela, come,' she tries to stand but is too worn out to move. Instead she takes my hand. 'I am so happy to see you, we have missed your smiling face so much, but you should not carry this burden. The fate of your family does not fall upon you alone, we are in this together. It is not your responsibility to send money, allow yourself to appreciate the opportunity you have been given, to learn, to be a child, to be healthy, to lead a wonderful life. It suits you.' She tips her chair slightly to look me up and down. 'You are blossoming, child. I am so pleased to see it.'

I throw my arms around her neck. I have missed her so much. She is a precious link to my fallen mother.

'I brought money, it isn't much, but it's all I have.' I empty my pockets, keeping only the precious bus ticket back to the Webbs.

'Thank you, sweetheart. It all helps.' She pockets my small change and takes my hand once more. 'Now tell me about your adventures before the others return.'

I tell her of Victoria Academy and the Webbs, about their house full of white and crisp and clean things, a dirt-free zone. She laughs and her eyes sparkle like they used to.

'Lela!' Juliet's voice shrieks as she sees me. 'My sister, I missed you!' She throws her soft arms around me. She has grown so much, and I am so pleased to see it. She looks well, and I worry again that Beatrice gives all the available food to her and her children, short-changing herself. Not for the first time, I pray there is a special place in heaven for her when her time comes.

'Have you seen Hope? And Ada?'

'Hope is doing so well at the orphanage. She's happy. Ada works hard, but they are a good family. She never has time to come back but sends some money and they feed her well. We are managing, Lela, I assure you, we are managing. I cannot say that life isn't hard. It is, food is short, I am growing too weak to work and must rely on the generosity of others, but for now we are ok.'

I nod, knowing that life in Bwaise is like that, you must take each day as it comes, and just hope the good ones outnumber the bad.

I glance at my watch and Beatrice smiles. 'Not staying long?' I hide it with my right hand, embarrassed.

'It's ok,' she soothes.

'They don't know I'm here.'

'I thought not. You go. We are ok. Thank you for the money.'

'I do not have time to see Jaaja, or Dembe, or Hope, can you tell them I will come again as soon as I can.'

'Of course, I will.' I hug Beatrice close, scared, as always, that it's for the last time. Juliet huddles in between us. I kiss her little face and tell her I love her.

I walk quickly to the bus stop, my eyes pricking, trying not to attract the attention of strangers. The visit was so short, but my time is running out. A bus pulls up to the stop as I approach. Some people climb on, but when it's my turn, the driver holds up his arm.

'I'm full, no more passengers.'

'Oh please, please,' I beg, 'I'm only small, I can squeeze on.' But he is resolute, and I am left alone once more on the edge of Bwaise, the sun sinking in the sultry sky.

By the time the next bus arrives, I know I will be very late. The hands on my luxurious wristwatch point to the six.

Mrs. Webb will be wanting to prepare that Dutch meal and I am ages away. She trusted me, gave me a chance to bond with her like a daughter and I threw it back in her face. I will be lucky if they want me back at all.

The bus journey lasts forever in the Kampala rush hour traffic, the manic roads at a standstill. Dinner time is over and the streetlamps are lit, moths bouncing off their luminous bulbs. The road is silent except for the humming of distant crickets over the gardens. I stop to remove my sandals, which have given me large blisters on my heels. When I finally get to the Webb's compound, the gates are wide open. A group is gathered at the entrance, torches in hand, three cars parked alongside. What has happened? I hold tightly to my shoes and run the last stretch. Why are so many people there? Has something happened to the Webbs? Then Mrs. Webb spots me.

'Oh Lela, thank God, where have you been? We were so worried.' She runs towards me, her arms outstretched, 'Thank heavens you are home.'

Home.

Chapter Thirty-Nine

'You went where?'

'Bwaise.'

'Bwaise!' she whispers. All Kampalans know of Bwaise and its horrors. 'Why?'

'I went to see my family,' I sigh, resigned to telling the truth.

'Your family?' Mrs. Webb pulls away, as though I had slapped her.

'I didn't tell you because I thought you would be angry.'

'I don't understand, we were told you are an orphan?'

'I am, my mother died of AIDS, I never knew my Father, I have sisters though and a brother, sometimes they, well, I must help them.'

'Oh Lela, I am so sorry, so very sorry.'

'Oh My.' Mr. Webb pats me on the shoulder and walks away, shaking his head.

'You are sorry?' Now it is my turn to be confused. 'I should have told you. After everything you have done for me, given me, how could I ask for more?'

'No Lela, we should have asked you.' Mrs. Webb holds my hand whilst Mr. Webb nods his agreement. 'We assumed that you were alone in this world. We didn't want to pry about your background.'

'Please don't send me back. I can't help them. They can't afford to feed me. My Jaaja is old, with cancer, and Beatrice...'

'Who is Beatrice?'

I tell them of her long friendship with my mother, everything she has ever done for us. They are fascinated, concerned. I see their eagerness to help. I am struck again with the force of their kindness, and the interrogation turns into a conversation.

'Bwaise isn't all bad,' I say, and tell them about the community spirit that endures despite all the privations, about Hope, happy in the orphanage, and the good people who run it. 'Ada, my eldest sister, has a cleaning job with a wealthy family. They work her hard, but they feed her. My brother, Dembe, lives with Jaaja, but her cancer means she cannot

221

care for him as she would like. He does not speak, so we cannot judge what kind of life he has had.' I tell them about his scars. Then I tell them about Elizabeth.

The Webbs close in around me, both holding me tight in a way that I had never been held before. I feel protected, safe.

'Lela, we have presumed to know what is best for you. It seemed so obvious, that you couldn't possibly need anything other than what we have given you. We would like you to take us to your family. Can you do that? We want to see where you grew up.'

'Yes, you can take me tomorrow. I would love you to know my family.'

The relief that they are not angry is overwhelming. That they want me to stay with them, continue my education *and* help my family. If they had decided to send me home, I would have returned without a negative word, but I wouldn't have been pirouetting with joy either.

I am awake and dressed before the sun has peeked over the horizon. As dawn arrives so does a crisp, clean, faultless sky. Another perfect Ugandan day. A pair of Kaloli birds perch on the compound wall, preening their thick black wings. They remind me of the trip to hospital with Maama, and I shudder. I am relieved it is not raining. Rain turns Bwaise into a marshland with raw sewage floating on the surface. I do not want the Webbs to have to traipse through scum. I wear my oldest dress, although with the Webbs on either side of me, I will stand out like a beacon. Mr. and Mrs. Webb are already awake, nursing large mugs of black coffee.

'Lela, dear, you are up early.'

'Yes, I couldn't sleep.'

'It seems it is a common malady. Can we get you some breakfast?'

None of us has much appetite. When we have finished picking at our food, Mr. Webb says; 'Are you ready? Let's not delay any longer,' he smiles, and collects a few personal objects from a bowl on the countertop.

Mrs. Webb fetches a basket from the larder, the contents hidden beneath a red and white checked tea towel. My sandals are too painful to wear, so I slip on my black school shoes instead, grateful for the familiar tread of the insoles. They will better protect my feet from the sewage.

We leave the city before rush hour and we reach the familiar roads in no time.

'Lela, I'm sorry, I don't know this area, is there ummm parking, somewhere?' I look at Mr. Webb, and then suddenly the three of us burst out laughing. 'Probably not, eh?' he chuckles. When we went to buy clothes, we left the car in a huge multi-story car park, three layers of cars all on top of each other. Bwaise has nothing like that.

I am suddenly worried about the car. We should have taken the bus. 'Umm, best park further out, the closer you get to the slums the more packed the houses become, and the streets are too narrow for a car. If you park too close to the centre of Bwaise, the wheels might be stolen.' Or the car, I think.

Mr. Webb parks outside the nearest church, I suppose hoping that God will protect it. I lead them to Beatrice's, all the while the streets around me become more enclosed, the buildings less like houses and more like shacks. Mrs. Webb is growing nervous, and she has taken her husband's arm for support. Hordes of young children are following us, chattering, laughing, and waving at us. A young girl has taken Mrs. Webb by the hand and is chatting excitedly about her doll. Mrs. Webb smiles at her but I know she cannot understand everything. The young girl is impressively fluent in Uglish, a mixture of English and Ugandan, much like many of the people here. Mrs. Webb nods maternally. Our entourage grows considerably as we reach the heart of Bwaise. It is early so the smell is not as bad, but it is not pleasant. Mrs. Webb searches in her handbag, under the hopeful eyes of the children. She pulls out both some tissues and a pack of sweets. The children cheer as she offers them the pack to share between themselves. She uses the tissue to cover her mouth and nose.

'How can they allow this?' she mutters to her husband. 'So much sewage, with all these little children around. It's a disaster waiting to happen.'

Mr. Webb shakes his head sadly in agreement.

'Just around here,' I point as we approach Beatrice's home. I am excited now. Beatrice is already up and about. She stands in the doorway sweeping the entrance. I am pleased that the Webbs are seeing her on a good day. She smiles at the strange procession.

'Lela, Lela!' It is Juliet, tugging at my sleeve.

'This is my little sister, Juliet,' I say to the Webbs.

'Hello Juliet! Mrs. Webb bends to Juliet's level and smiles, but she takes in the dirt on her cotton dress, more a pillowcase with holes for her arms. The bare feet, covered in mud, or worse. Her hair is so matted it has been tied tightly to her scalp to hide it. To me, Juliet looks well, but how can I explain this? I suddenly regret bringing them here. I fear they are judging my family, judging my life and I am not prepared for it.

Beatrice rests her hand on the cool section of corrugated iron making up a wall and straightens her skirt, clearly gathering her strength. She takes in a deep breath and steels herself to stand unaided once more. She ambles towards us.

'Good morning, I am Beatrice.' She offers her hand to the Webbs.

'Hello Beatrice, I am so sorry to spring our arrival on you. We wanted to meet Lela's family.'

'Well of course, come in, can I offer you some tea?' I am proud of her generosity, as she has so very little to give.

'Oh no, do not worry about us, we are only stopping to say hello!'

She relaxes a little, although clearly in pain.

'Is it bad?' Mrs. Webb gently rests her hand upon Beatrice's arm. Beatrice stiffens, then suddenly the tears come, probably in the face of such unexpected kindness.

'My dear, oh my dear, let us take you inside,' Mrs. Webb takes Beatrice's full weight against her arm, steering her through the opening. Juliet has claimed Mr. Webb by slipping her tiny hand in his. Next to his staggering height I see the Juliet they see, a tiny, frail little girl, especially filthy next to the Webb's signature starched cotton.

Half an hour later, there is a carnival atmosphere at Beatrice's, a collection of misfits, outcasts and orphans. Outside the hut the crowd has not yet dispersed. The sudden appearance of two elegant Europeans is not to be ignored and they still linger nearby in the hope of some entertainment. Children kick empty cans to one another. Men lean against surrounding shacks, smoking and laughing, determined not to miss anything of interest. The women retire into the shade to breastfeed or rock their sweating infants, but they also keep a close eye on our strange gathering.

I look around the sea of faces, such an odd collection of people, all joined together because of me. Beatrice sits in prime position, near the back wall of her shack, with the Webbs on either side. Jaaja has arrived after a small boy was given a handful of change to go and call for her. She brought my brother, Dembe, who hangs near the doorway, unable to find the courage to step closer. The boy lingers, hoping for another errand. He has made more money this morning than he ever has in his life. He stares at Dembe, trying to understand why he does not talk. Dembe has grown, and has stopped soiling himself, but he still withdraws from attention and affection. I wonder again at the horrors he has witnessed. I have been raped, abused, bullied, starved and I have seen death at close quarters, yet I wish I could reassure him that not all people are bad.

The adults use words I cannot wholly understand. 'Protection orders' 'Safeguarding.' They look at Dembe, me and Juliet often. I miss Ada. We wanted to call for her too, but she can only leave work in an emergency. In Uganda, that means death.

So, you think that would be best for Dembe?' I overhear Mr. Webb asking. Hearing his name, Dembe turns on his heels and heads out of the door. I make my escape too, uncomfortable that my future is being discussed without my own input. I try to appreciate it, to allow the heavy responsibility to fall on someone else for a change.

Outside, the midday sun is glaring. The smell is immense now. I fear Mrs. Webb will not cope as even I have to switch my breathing from nasal to oral. I look for my brother. He has not gone far. He is always afraid and sticks close to what he knows.

225

I approach him carefully. I have not earned his trust yet. He does not know me. For him, simple blood ties don't mean much.

'Dembe,' I speak his name gently. He kicks haphazardly at some weeds fighting for survival under layers of dust and rock. He stops.

'Dembe, I know these people are strangers to you, that they are making plans for us without consulting us, and that can't be easy to hear. They are such kind people and they wish to help us.' He looks at me, directly in the eye for the first time ever. I realise he is questioning me.

'They have treated me so well, like a daughter. They follow God's lead. I trust them, and I hope you can trust me, your sister.' His gaze returns to the lump of weeds. His hands are shaking.

'Brother, what happened to you?' I reach out to touch the scars on his arm. They are old and healed over, but they stand out like tattoos. He flinches and draws his arm away. 'Dembe, I only want to help.' I feel suddenly weary, the excitement and anxiety of bringing the Webbs to Bwaise has worn off and my stomach is rumbling. Overhead a dense humidity is taking over. The sky, so perfectly cobalt this morning, is now covered with hazy cloud. The air is thick, not a leaf stirs. I wait for him to respond. I wish I could tell him his suffering is over, but he is locked into his own little world. Somewhere in the distance there is a low grumbling of thunder, so I almost miss my mute brother mumbling something.

'Leela' He is looking directly at me once more, 'Leela?'

'Yes, yes my brother.' I take his arm, excited to make a connection with him.

'Leela.'

'Lela, I think we are ready to go now, if you'd like to say goodbye?' Mr. Webb stoops to emerge from the doorway. Dembe pulls his arm away, retreating as far as he can from the tall white man. I try to approach him again, but he turns his back on me. My chance to gain his trust has passed.

Beatrice hugs me close. 'You did well, child, your Maama would be so proud of you, thank you child, thank you.'

'I haven't done anything,' I protest. It is true, the Webbs have done everything.

'You have done more than you could ever know, Lela,' My Jaaja confirms this and pulls me close to her. My head no longer meets her chest. We are almost the same height now and I wonder if I have grown, or if she has shrunk. Her shoulder blades are sharp as I embrace her. I have the familiar fear that this is the last goodbye.

Chapter Forty

I am going to a new school. My 'good deed' of taking the
Webbs to visit my family had repercussions for me, more
mouths to feed, more children needing teaching obviously
costs more money. The Victoria Academy fees do not come
cheap. Of course, I am glad for my family, but I cannot lie, I
am heartsore for myself. I tell myself I am being selfish, but
how I loved my time at Victoria Academy, and the friends I
made there. I pack up the uniform, ready for its new owner. I
think about the girl destined to open this box, a sponsor no
doubt, like me. The rich students wouldn't dream of wearing
secondhand clothes. How much has changed, yet again, in
such a short space of time.

My new uniform isn't bad, there was a time, not so long
ago, when I would have begged for clean clothes on my
back, a place at school, any school, just to have the
opportunity to learn. I now have all these things, but my
heart is heavy, though I try to hide it. I'm wearing a plain
grey skirt and a white shirt. Mrs. Webb has ironed it to
perfection, each fold sharp. It smells, as all her clothes do, like
jasmine. The rest of my school belongings sit on my neatly
made bed. All my other Victoria Academy belongings stay
with me, my satchel, my notebooks, my assortment of
pencils. My feet have grown over the summer, so Mr. Webb
took me shopping for a smart pair of leather shoes, he called
them 'brogues.' I cannot help but admire their shine.

'Are you ready, Lela?' Mrs. Webb calls me from the hall.

'I'm coming.'

I collect my belongings, glancing around the lovely room
I have come to call my own.

Mr. Webb loads my case into the back of his car. Mrs.
Webb is not planning on making this journey with me,
because she is expecting visitors.

'It was lovely of you to have me to stay,' I hold my hand
out.

'Lela, you funny thing, come here.' She pulls me close
and holds me. When she lets me go, I see she is crying.

'Mrs. Webb are you ok?'

'Of course, my child, just sad to see you go, I have become so accustomed to your sunny self around the house. The house will feel quite empty without you.'

I am touched at so much warmth and tears rush to my eyes.

'You are part of the family Lela, we told you that from the start.' She seems to understand how much reassurance I need. I hope we'll see you before the end of term too, God willing.'

'God willing,' I repeat and smile. I chide myself for doubting them.

It's not a long journey. Mr. Webb has allowed me to sit in the front of his car. The view from here is quite spectacular. The rain is brewing, there is a heavy, humid feeling to the air and even with the front window open there is very little breeze. We slow to a standstill when we get to the local market. A bicycle weighed down with a hundred pineapples swerves in and out of the traffic, expertly avoiding runaway poultry and a mangy black cat licking itself. His tyre clunks heavily in a nearby pothole. He puts a foot down to steady himself then rides on. Women stroll in front of the car, their heads piled high with fruit and other goods. Mr. Webb anticipates a long wait and turns off the engine. I hang my head out of the car window to absorb the atmosphere. My nose picks up the distinct smell of fried egg and cabbage, someone is making a Rolex. My stomach grumbles noisily, despite my large breakfast. They are a favourite. Mr. Webb laughs.

'We may be here a while, fancy a snack?'

I laugh too, embarrassed. 'No, don't worry, I just love that smell.'

'Well, you might want to stock up on some snacks. For school?'

'They feed us well at school.'

'You don't know what the new place is like.'

I hadn't thought of that. The crowd finally parts and Mr. Webb puts his car into gear.

'Have you seen the school, Mr. Webb?'

'Only in photos. I wish we'd had the chance to see it. My colleague's daughter goes there, and she does very well. I

230

hope it will be good for you. It's a lot more affordable now we are helping your brother with school too.'

I nod. I am grateful to be going to school at all. Dembe's school is astonishingly expensive, as he needs so much extra support. He plays on my mind. The Webbs did a lot of research finding a school suitable for his unique problems. I hope they treat him kindly. I wish I had heard what he had tried to tell me.

When we arrive, we are faced with the usual hubbub of the first day of term. A tall Ugandan man, who I assume is a teacher, is herding groups of children through the main entrance, encouraging the pupils to say a quick goodbye to their parents. The first day at Victoria Academy had had a carnival vibe, but here the children are quiet, subdued, each seeming to know exactly where they should be going and what they should be doing. One young boy clings to his mother while staring solemnly at the teacher. His mother strokes his hair, reluctant to let him go, but at last the father insists, pulling the boy away from her and adding him to the line slowly meandering into school.

'Well, this is it, how do you feel?' Mr. Webb looks down at me. A knot is forming in my stomach.

'I'll be fine,' I say.

'That's the spirit,' he says, and gives me a bear hug, rather awkward for his height, before climbing back into the car.

I wave as he pulls away. I approach the teacher, who reminds me of a policeman, directing traffic.

'Excuse me, I am new, please can you tell me which way I need to go.'

He looks down at me, a small smile forming in one corner of his mouth.

'Not your father, is he?' He nods in the direction of Mr. Webb' car, soon to be out of sight.

'He's my sponsor,' I reply, mildly confused.

'Oh, your *sponsor*, one of those then are you?' He nods as though affirming something in his mind. 'Just follow the girls, they will show you where to go.' I join the slow-moving queue into the ugly concrete building. After a few steps, the boys file off to the left, girls to the right. The girl in front of me is about my age. Maybe we'll bunk together.

'Hello, I'm Lela,' I pat her on the shoulder. She frowns.

'Shh,' She whispers, her finger to her lips, and points at the teacher before turning her back on me.

I feel I am filing into a funeral, not a school. I wish Mr. Webb could have stayed a little longer. Next to me the little boy who had clung to his mother stands with a poker straight back, clutching a solitary bag with both hands. He does not make a sound, but tears fall steadily down his cheeks. I reach out to stroke his shoulder. He shakes his head in fear, signaling that the teacher is right behind us. Is he another of the men I have learnt to fear?

Through the heavy iron front doors, we filter into a large rectangular room, like the main room of Hope's orphanage. A huge chalkboard takes up the entire wall furthest from me. The rest of the walls are plain concrete, some with cracks, the floor too. Here and there are long wooden trestle tables. A dozen or so stools circle each bench. This must be the main classroom. There are too many children for this one room, surely?

I shuffle forward with the crowd. Along with the other girls, I am slowly maneuvering into a room crowded with beds which leads to another dorm, equally crammed. As soon as the teacher is out of sight, the girls squabble for the best beds. The oldest girls take claim to the beds furthest from the window, the other girls fight for what is left. I earmark a rickety looking bedstead under the window which no one seems to want. I am happy to have it, as I would rather stare at the moon and the starlit sky than more cracks on a wall. I perch my suitcase on the end of my bed and open it, then search the space around me for any sign of drawers to put my belongings in. The room has grown silent again. The older girls congregate in a corner and stare at us new ones, including me.

'Hello, I'm new, could you tell me where I put my clothes?' Silence. I am surrounded by a sea of surly, hostile faces. The younger girls closely watch the older ones. A tall girl weaves her way in and out of the rows of beds. She is beautiful, so tall, her black hair long and tied in a bow at the back of her head. She smiles, showing straight and gleaming white teeth. She is like a cat gleefully stalking a mouse.

232

'Your clothes?' She speaks loudly, 'Well just how many clothes do you have?' Her friends giggle, though I don't see what's funny.

'Just my uniforms?' I say, confused.

'Uniforms? Are you planning on getting very dirty?' She has reached my bed now; her long legs bare under her school skirt. She tentatively picks up one of my pressed school shirts with her index finger. She holds it high.

'Well, this is very clean, but you must get filthy dirty to have so many, and so many skirts too? Do you soil yourself? I don't see why else you would need to change so often?' I snatch back my shirt, bewildered.

'Oh, touchy.' She forms her mouth into a perfect circle and covers it in a dramatic swoop of her hand, much like people in the television do. The room is awash with laughter now. The tall girl flips the lid of my case shut again and with a look of disgust eyes a small Victoria Academy emblem on my name tag.

'Well, umm, Lela is it? We keep our cases under our beds. If you have too much stuff to fit there, you'll just have to bin it, won't you? And refrain from soiling yourself, it is very unladylike,' She tosses her hair and strides back to her friends.

'Ignore her.' The bed alongside mine has been filled by another girl who quickly tucks her own similar sized suitcase under the bed. 'You a sponsor?' She lowers her voice.

'Umm, I have a sponsor if that's what you mean.'

'Shh. They hate sponsors here, I'm afraid it will cause you some trouble.'

'But why?'

'They think we are more privileged, that we have it easy, that we haven't worked for our belongings. I think it escapes their notice that for us to need sponsors we have had to hit rock bottom.'

'So, you have a sponsor too?' I whisper.

'Yes, I've been here two years. I can't say it gets any easier, but stick with me, at least we will have each other,' she smiles. Somewhere, a bell is ringing. The room falls silent and the girls rush to form a neat line, facing the door.

'Well, back to it,' The other sponsor girl mouths as we join the line.

'Lessons, already? I don't even know where the latrine is,' I whisper.

'Well best you hold it in, don't poo yourself *Sponsor*,' says my tormentor. The room erupts with laughter again before the teacher yells for silence.

Chapter Forty-One

'It's basic mathematics Lela, what's the matter? Your sponsor can't hold your hand for your entire life, you know.'

I am at the front of the classroom, my cheeks burning with humiliation. The entire school, bar the very youngest children, are behind me. I hear sniggering, despite the strict rule for silence. Mr. Zuluka takes pleasure in sneering at me. There are two long numbers on the chalk board. He wants me to multiply them together. I have not been taught how to do it. He does not show me the method, instead he likes to ridicule me. He grows impatient, but we both know he will not get the answer he is looking for.

He sends me back to my seat. 'It's hard to see how you will ever amount to anything. You should have stayed on the streets.'

I have learnt not to cry in the eight weeks since I arrived. Even so, the tears are welling up and I am furious with myself for showing my pain. Rosie, my sponsor friend, has her face to the wall as a punishment. This happens almost every lesson. She is clever, gets the grades, but he always finds a reason to punish her. Today it is for helping me. He likes to rap our fists with his ruler. He does it suddenly, with no warning, so we can't stop ourselves from yelping in pain. We try not to cry, but the pain is terrible. She will be there until lunch, at least another thirty minutes away.

The girls behind me whisper to each other. They never get beaten. Kizza and her gang; Ntongo, Tembo and Sara are worshipped in the school. The teachers do not touch them no matter the trouble they cause. They are the prettiest, the tallest. They are rich or pretend to be. Since my arrival, they have dedicated themselves to making my life as miserable as Rosie's. They have taken scissors to my new brogues, cutting the laces and slicing the soles. They have stolen my underwear and hung it out of the windows. They persist in calling me names, and slap and push me whenever the teachers are out of view. I try to ignore them, to concentrate on the work, but it is hard, and I must be wary of their constant schemes.

I glance at the clock. It will be lunchtime soon and then we have another teacher, Mr. Adisa. He is kind to me and helps me with each lesson, knowing I need more attention to catch up. I can survive the afternoon with Mr. Adisa in charge. My stomach rumbles, it has been a long morning and I have grown hungry. We work longer hours than we ever did at Victoria Academy. There is no time for fun here either, no drama, very little sports. The school gets good academic results, and no wonder, as we do nothing else but work.

The day begins at four am, even at the weekend. Mr. Zuluka wakes us, standing at the door of the dormitory ringing his large brass bell. We get five minutes to dress and another five to queue for the latrine. At that time in the morning the sky is still dark, and the air is cold. We shiver in our flimsy uniforms. If we do not make the queue quick enough, we do not have time to use the latrine. If we are desperate and must go, then we are late and get beaten. We work each morning until the sun rises then we get a break for breakfast, from seven am we are back at our desks ready for a full morning of work, bar a short mid-morning break. Lunch is at one pm for an hour then it is back to work until five pm. Dinner break is the longest, from five until seven, but we also must shower in that time and prepare our books for the following day. Then it is back to work until half ten when we are finally allowed to tumble into our beds, all of us exhausted, only to repeat the whole thing the next day.

I am so unhappy.

My grades are terrible, and I do not feel I am improving, despite my hard work. I dread what the Webbs will say when I see them for the holidays. I am so ashamed I am not doing better.

At last the bell peals and we file into the dinner hall, a long narrow room where the tables are positioned in two lines. The other children race to reach the front of the queue, so that their food will be plentiful and hot. I linger at the back of the room, not wishing to draw any more attention to myself today. The food here is OK, even the leftovers are not so bad. Rosie joins me, it seems she has the same idea. Kizza and her followers are already sitting down, the crowd always

236

makes room for them so they can get food first, as if she were Moses parting the Red Sea. She and her cronies are deep in quiet conversation, eyeballing me.

'She is planning something,' I whisper to Rosie.

'I know,' sighs Rosie.

'It must be bad this time.'

'Don't let her get you down.' She pats me on the shoulder sympathetically.

Kizza shouts out.

'Hey, sponsor, don't eat too much ehh, you don't want to poo yourself again.' This has become her running joke, so predictable, yet her friends erupt in laughter. They are soon whispering again.

When I am finished, I return my cup and plate to the kitchen, thanking the dinner ladies and decide to spend the remainder of my lunch break lying on my bed under the sunny window. I learnt on my first night why no one else wanted the window beds. The windows do not close properly, and the cold night air blows right through the skinny single bedsheet. However, during the day I can lie and look up at the clear skies and the birds hovering high above me. As soon as I walk into the dormitory, I smell something putrid. I see there is a damp, dirty patch seeping through my sheets. My bed is filled with faeces, actual human excrement. The smell is unbearable. I place my hand over my mouth and nose, yet nothing stops the stench. I gag. I can't help myself.

'Ohh look, sponsor messed her bed,' comes the sly voice of Kizza, sneering in delight. She and her cronies giggle, but they can't stay to enjoy their triumph, as the appalling stink is too much for them to bear.

How I want to slap her, to scratch that perfect face of hers, to make her as ugly on the outside as she is on the inside, but I must escape the dorm. I go to the latrine, the only place I get any privacy and vomit up my meal, resting my forehead on the toilet to cry tears of fury and frustration.

'I am better off here, I have food, I am learning,' I repeat this mantra to remind myself that good things are happening, this is the path that God has chosen for me. But I only sob harder.

I splash my face with water, and steel myself to go and face my defiled bed. I am already in trouble, late for afternoon lessons. I may as well be even later. It's worth it for a clean bed tonight. Really, I have no alternative. The dormitory reeks as I approach. Kizza and her gang will have to live with the smell too. Stupid as well as cruel. I peel away the sheets carefully, ensuring I do not tip the contents over any of my belongings and drag the bedding into the yard to the water pump. I empty the stools in the dirt and kick sand over them, then place my sheets under the pump, pulling the lever to expel fresh water over my bedding. The water gushes out and splashes up at me. I flinch, hoping nothing ricochets onto my clothing, brushing the loose strands of my hair away from my face. I spy a pair of black eyes watching me from a shaded corner of the yard. I look up with a face of fury, expecting to see one of my tormentors.

Out of the shade, a skinny boy of my age steps into the light. His hair is disheveled and there is dirt on his face. His bare feet are filthy. He looks troubled, his forehead creased with lines of worry. I do not know him, but the girls and boys do not mix so often, so that is not so strange.

'What are you looking at?' I ask aggressively.

'I just want to ask you how you do it. How do you remain so strong? They torment you every day, but all the time you keep positive, and show them you are better. Perhaps that's why they hate you so much.'

My eyes smart from his unexpectedly kind words, but I have learned not to take things at face value.

'Do I look positive?' I scoff, glaring at my soiled sheets and my soaking school uniform.

'I see you, every day, you get up and go to lessons, you put up with every vile thing those girls do to you, every slur that the teacher throws, but you keep going. Me? I hide out here, I cannot face it every day.'

'You hide? And you get away with it?'

'Mostly.' He shrugs, 'Lucky for me they are usually too preoccupied with what you are doing.'

I nod then return to the sheets.

'Let me help you.' He bends down and starts scrubbing with handfuls of grass, dried out under the hot sun. It works surprisingly well.

'You don't have to do that,' I insist, though I am secretly grateful.

'I want to, you don't deserve this.'

I smile apprehensively, not quite trusting that there is kindness here.

'I am Abdullah,' the two of us are about to shake hands, then both decide against it. We laugh.

'Lela,' We wave at each other instead.

We scrub with the dried grass in silence for quite some time, the sun burning the back of our necks, until, at last, they come clean.

'So, tell me your secret? I've run away before, my family live nearby, but my father just keeps returning me here, telling me I will bring shame on the family if I give up my schooling.'

'I suppose it's God's will that keeps me going. This is all part of his plan for me, and if I keep faith everything will work out for the best.'

He ponders this for a moment.

'My father prays to Allah, he prays on a mat five times a day, I have tried, but I do not think it is working.'

'I am lucky. I guess my God is listening.'

'I wish mine would,' he stares into the open door of the school, the echo of the lesson in progress.

'It will be dinner soon. You can't stay out here all night.'

'I can go often without eating, I am used to it.'

'I have gone hungry too many times to miss a meal if I can help it,' I say. 'Come into dinner with me. Being seen with me will probably make things worse for you, but we can at least be together.'

'You would do that for me?'

'Yes. I would do that for someone who rolled his sleeves up and helped me clean up this awful mess. That makes you the best friend I have in all the world right now.'

'I'm... your friend?'

'Yes.'

239

'Well then, let me help you with this.' He picks up the opposite corner of my bedsheet. He flaps it up and down in the sunlight, making it into a sail. We race around the playground together, the sheet blowing wildly around us. I begin to laugh, something I haven't done for a long time. We both squeal in delight and then laugh even harder recalling how this whole situation began. Who would have thought that something so vile could bring such fun?

My sheet is quickly dried in the hot air and together we tiptoe back into the girls' dormitory. Luckily for us, the coast is clear. If Abdullah was found in here, we would both be expelled. He examines my mattress, now stained.

'Well this isn't pretty.' He approaches it and turns away. 'Urgh, it smells awful, you can't sleep on this.'

'We could turn it?' I suggest.

He looks around the dormitory, then his eyes widen in delight as a thought hits him. 'Which is her bed?'

'Her?'

'You know, the tall evil one.'

'Kizza?'

That's the one.'

I point to her bed on the far side of the room.

'How long do you think we have until the bell rings?'

'Ten minutes.'

'That will do.' He yanks my mattress from its old bedstead.

'You're not?' I gasp as I realise what he's doing.

'Help me,' he says. I obey, giggling. I know it's wrong, but she deserves it.

Working together we swap the two mattresses and make both beds before escaping the dorm for dinner. The others snigger as they see me coming but I don't care. I have found a friend.

240

It's after lights out. I had the expected jibes as we got ready for bed, 'Enjoy your soiled sheets, sponsor', and other equally intelligent remarks, but I keep my secret to myself. My bed sheets do not smell as fresh as daisies. They needed scalding water, plenty of soap and bleach. I try to get to sleep, feeling vaguely unclean.

'I can smell you from over here, sponsor,' Kizza continues, determined to mine this rich seam of humour for all its worth. Her cronies giggle into their pillows. She smells the air noisily. Even the younger ones snigger, afraid that if they do not, she will turn on them. I smile to myself in the dark.

The laughter suddenly stops. My heart stops at the same time. It has clicked.

'Sponsor, no! You better not have!' She shouts suddenly. She leaps from her bed as if it contained a crocodile and rips the sheets off it. I am busted.

'You have, you have!' she screams. I hear rapid footsteps approaching. If it is Zuluka I am as good as dead.

'What's going on in here?' It is Adisa. Thank God. I remain frozen to the spot and close my eyes tightly, pretending to be asleep. God knows I've had to do *that* often enough in the past.

'Kizza, what are you doing, girl?' He loiters at the entrance. 'What is that smell?'

'That girl *shit* her bed and swapped *her* mattress with *mine*!' She screams as she points accusingly at me.

'I do not like your tone, girl. Do not use that language in front of me. You will have to answer to your parents. Now explain what is going on.'

As abruptly as it erupted, her tantrum ends. Her voice wavers as though she is close to tears.

'Sponsor...' she begins.

'I do not know who sponsor is,' Mr. Adisa interrupts.

'Her, that *thing* under the window,' she spits, her voice is full of venom.

'I believe she has a name.'

'Lela,' she forces herself to say it.

241

'So, what has Lela done? She looks as though she is sleeping peacefully.'

'She *always* messes herself.' No one laughs. 'And this time she swapped *her* mattress with *mine!*'

He says nothing. It is a clever trap, as she feels compelled to continue speaking. 'She hates me. She hits me, and kicks me, and punches me. Sara,' she appeals to her friend. 'Tell him.'

Sara is silent. She knows a sinking ship when she sees one, and she isn't climbing on board.

'We both know that is a lie, Kizza. If you have had an accident, girl, then for goodness sake clean yourself up. Stop blaming it on someone else just because you are embarrassed. You are more than old enough to sort yourself out.' A few of the younger girls are unable to stop themselves from giggling.

'That's enough, all of you,' he says, returning the room to silence. 'I shall remain in the hallway until you are all asleep. Any more noise and your parents will be notified, do I make myself clear?' He turns back to Kizza. 'Make your bed and get in it, child.'

Kizza reluctantly obeys. I continue to feign sleep but inside my body there is a party in full swing.

At last exhaustion catches up with me as I watch the ghostly moon climb higher in the sky. Mr. Adisa is still in the corridor. Every now and then he clears his throat, and noisily leafs through his papers, to remind us that he is there. Before I give in to sleep, I hear a vicious whisper in my ear.

'*You are dead, Sponsor.*'

I cannot keep Mattress-gate to myself, and Abdullah high fives me at the breakfast table as I regale him with the evening's events. Even Rosie smiles over her breakfast. Kizza's hair is tousled, and she has bags under her eyes. I see her watching me, plotting her revenge. I see it written all over her face and I shall have to watch my step over the coming days. For once, I feel blessed that there is not much privacy here, and very few places where she can corner me alone without a teacher near.

Mr. Adisa is watching me too. He leans against the concrete, his head tipped backwards. He looks as exhausted as

242

Kizza and I wonder how long he stayed in the hallway. As I had pretended to be asleep, I can't even thank him without implicating myself. I nod at him in politeness instead, and mentally prepare myself for a morning of humiliation with Zuluka.

I saunter into the classroom following breakfast with a new-found confidence. If I can accomplish a win over Kizza then maybe, one day, I'll do the same over Zuluka. Mr. Adisa had presided over the sunrise session, that hideous lesson where we sit at our desks in darkness, attempting to learn when all we want to do is sleep. Now it is time for Zuluka, and Kizza and her cronies are right behind me.

'Sponsor is a dead girl,' she mutters. On the same day I made a true friend, I have also made a sworn enemy.

'Silence,' Zuluka spits over our heads as he stalks in, on the warpath as usual. We sit bolt upright.

'So. I just had a little look at yesterday's register. It seems two of your decided to flunk off classes.' My confidence immediately evaporates, and I feel a stab of fear. At least Abdullah is with me now. Zuluka turns his back to the class, rummaging in the chalk tray for a decent sized piece. I glance behind me to try and catch Abdullah's eye. Kizza stares and pokes her tongue at me

'You! Sponsor! I feel something hard hit the back of my head. Zuluka has thrown the chalk duster at me. I smart in shock.

'Did I give you permission to chat to Kizza?'

'Oh, trust me, I wasn't.' The words shoot from my mouth before I have properly considered them.

'Oh, I suppose Kizza, like the rest of us, isn't good enough for you?'

'No, I…' He dares me to continue. I do not.

'As I was saying. Two of you missed Mr. Adisa's very intellectual Maths Quiz yesterday… the identity of one of the truants should come as no surprise. Lela, if you could please grace me with your presence here up front.' I reluctantly rise from my desk and make my way down the aisle as slowly as I dare. I stand beside Zuluka.

'Abdullah, you too boy.' Abdullah rises from his desk. He glances at the doorway, clearly tempted to run, but good sense prevails, and he joins me up front.

His eyes briefly meet mine. I try to show strength, but my hands are shaking with awful anticipation.

'Hands out.' I hold my hands up, as does Abdullah. Zuluka pushes our hands together and with a quick swipe brings his ruler down onto our fists, hitting us both at the same time.

'Together in truancy, together in punishment. Abdullah, you should choose your friends more carefully.'

Abdullah looks me straight in the eye. I cannot hold my tears in. They drip down my face and begin to land on our intertwined, bloodstained hands.

'You can't choose your family, but you can choose your friends.' Abdullah's voice quivers over another crack of the whip. 'And I choose Lela.'

I manage to smile through the pain.

'Sit down, the pair of you disgust me.' Abdullah leads me back to my seat. I am grateful, as my feet are unsteady. Zuluka cannot resist flinging another barb at us.

'Don't expect to be fed today. Instead, you can scrub this floor during your lunch break.'

So, we scrub through lunch time and we scrub through dinner time. Zuluka watches us like a vulture throughout, so we are forced to work in silence, afraid to even glance at each other. The food here is not wonderful, but food is food, and we are both ravenous. At last, the vulture leaves to do his dormitory rounds and we can breathe again.

'The tyrant,' Abdullah sneers, but in a whisper.

The dining tables are now pushed back against the walls, but there is a scribbled note at the end of one table, alongside two lonely looking mugs.

Lela and Abdullah, Thought you could do with these. Sleep well.

'I wonder who left these for us?' The corridors are now silent and the dorms in darkness.

'Mr. Adisa maybe?' says Abdullah. 'He has some decency in him.'

'But I don't think he is on duty tonight?'

'It's still hot. Come on, Lela, it will be better than going to bed with nothing.'

Abdullah pulls a bench closer and we sit side by side in the abandoned hall. He gulps at his mug of porridge noisily. Mine is still too hot for me. I warm my fingers on it as I blow softly on the surface.

'I have been thinking about what you said yesterday, about how God's will keeps you strong.'

'Yes?'

'Well, how can you be sure your God has you on the right path? What if this is nothing but a terrible time? What if there is no purpose to it?'

'I can't believe that. This is just part of my journey. God helps us all when the time is right. Maybe he is preparing me for something. He has saved me before and he will save me from this. If not on Earth, then when I die and go to Heaven.'

'Heaven?'

'It is the place we go when we die. God takes us into his kingdom of Heaven, it is paradise, death is never something to fear.'

'But how do you know that God will take you, that it even exists?'

'God sent his own son, Jesus, to Earth to help us all and he died a horrible brutal death, but then he rose again, and he went to Heaven, where he lives now. He died so we can be forgiven. It is quite complicated, but I can show you in my bible someday.'

'I don't fully understand.' He stares at the remainder of his hot porridge. 'But I like the sound of your God. I like the idea of being saved and going to Heaven.'

'It is reassuring at times like this, for sure.'

'Could you teach me, Lela? Teach me the stories from your holy book? I want to know. I want to follow your God.'

'Really?'

'I would like to if you don't mind?'

'Of course, I don't mind'

'Eat up, before it gets cold. We'd best get to bed before Zuluka returns.' I nod and gulp down the thick, gooey oats, keen to finish before Zuluka heads back to us. The porridge is almost gone when I am suddenly caught by an uncomfortable sharpness in my chest.

'Are you ok?'

'It burns…' I whisper as the pain intensifies.

'Well, it will if you knock it back that fast,' he sniggers and drains the last of his cup. My chest feels as though it is on fire, my stomach burns. The porridge rises, but I can't be sick. Everything hurts. I trip backwards over the bench, clutching at my throat, desperate to inhale, but I cannot breathe, I land heavily on my back. Abdullah is shouting at me, his face contorted with worry, but the blood is rushing to my ears and I can't hear him. He claws at my hands stuck to my throat, then starts to shout for help. His panicked face is the last thing I remember.

Chapter Forty-Three

'Lela?' I hear a voice, male, soft and calm somewhere in the distance. Everything hurts, my throat is raw, I try to groan but it is too sore to even make a noise. 'Lela, sweetheart, can you open your eyes?' I try, and they open a slit, but I am blinded by a bright white light.

'Everything will be very strange for her for a while. She just needs time.' A woman's voice this time.

'Yes, thank you, I understand.' I still cannot place his voice and so re-open my eyes. I blink furiously to adjust to the light. It is Mr. Adisa. There is no sign of Abdullah. I am pinned down by wires and tubes protruding from my nose.

'There you are,' Mr. Adisa smiles, 'Now take it easy, everything will be very sore.'

I am in a hospital. My bed is in a children's ward, but it is quiet, and the people around me speak in low voices. There are machines everywhere and they beep continuously. Do the Webbs know I am here? Are they nearby?

'Lela, there was an accident. It seems you ate porridge which, somehow, I cannot comprehend how, had glass in it. We have tried to find out how it got there. You have been very ill. We were worried you might not pull through. The doctors here worked tirelessly to save you, there was a lot of bleeding inside you, but you will recover now. Lela, I fear Abdullah had something to do with it. His porridge was fine.'

I shake my head. I know that he is my friend and would never hurt me.

'Shh, stay calm.' He strokes my hair to stop me struggling. When I am able to talk, I will tell him he is wrong.

'Listen, Lela, we made a lot of enquiries after the accident, and we now know that you have been a target. Not only for the students, but the teachers too. You are a sweet girl, and I do not wish anything like this to happen to you again. Your sponsors have been away but will be here soon to visit you. But Lela, they are not at the school to protect you.'

I do not attempt to move again; I feel like I am being stabbed. I want to see the Webbs so badly. I desperately hope they will remove me from this terrible school completely. If only they could take Abdullah too. Another waif and stray to add to their collection.

'I can offer you protection,' Adisa continues. 'I can take you under my wing and the teachers would not touch you, and neither would Kizza and her friends. Do you understand? Blink once if you understand me.'

I blink. He moves closer. I can smell lunch on his breath.

'I will look after you from now on, but you must do something for me.' I blink again.

'You must promise me you will not see that Abdullah boy again. I do not trust him. He is not a suitable friend for you, his father tells me stories, but I will not trouble you with those' I try my best not to blink this time, as I cannot protest. Instead I shake my head as I feel the tears rising, and my painful throat constricts. To have protection would be a wonderful thing, but Abdullah is my only true friend. When I am better, I can explain that Abdullah is good, that he would never grind glass in anyone's food, let alone mine. I hold my eyes open for as long as I can, but eventually I blink. I cannot help it.

He takes my hand and kisses it. 'I'm so happy you have agreed to this, Lela. I really look forward to looking after you. I have to get back to school now, but I will see you again soon.'

Three weeks later and I am walking out of hospital on my own two legs, breathing the humid Kampala air by myself. There was a heavy rain overnight, but the clouds have dispersed and the world shimmers, sunlight catching every raindrop resting on the leaves. The palms look golden, the intense blue of the sky reflected in the puddles, making the street appear blue too. As promised, Mr. Adisa is by my side. He is pushing a wheelchair, but I walk confidently, grateful to feel the sun on my skin again.

'You worry too much,' I tell him.

'It is my job,' he smiles. I am thinking of Abdullah. I want to tell him how God saved me, just as I told him he would. Something bad happened, but it was God's will that sent me Adisa, an angel to protect me from hatred. With him by my side I do not worry about returning, I am pleased I might have a chance to see my friend. I have tried to tell Adisa it was Kizza that did this to me, but he is resolute. Her words 'You are dead, sponsor' swim around my head. God will protect me; I assure myself as I step into the rickety looking Ford parked by the hospital entrance.

As we approach the school building, a small cluster of girls gather by the doors, holding a banner welcoming me 'home.' I smile at the gesture. I am touched they have thought of me. Abdullah is nowhere to be seen. Mr. Adisa holds my arm protectively, although I do not need it.

'You don't have to go to lessons until tomorrow. You rest now.' He walks me to the entrance of the dorm and tells me he will see me later.

I sit on my bed alone, and breathe in the smell of the dorm, an odd mixture of shampoo, laundry detergent and feet. Nothing has changed in my absence. I inspect my belongings, sure to find them tampered with while I was gone. My spare shoes are missing, the pretty sandals the Webbs had bought me in the summer. Below my nightdress my Bible is wrapped safely. It is my most prized possession. I lie on top of the fresh sheets, which thankfully are new and smell of the outdoors. Flicking through the pages of my bible, I look for a passage to inspire me, but Abdullah is on my mind.

I check the hall to ensure Mr. Adisa is not lingering, and walk quietly out of the back door, in the direction of the latrines. My eyes search the shadows, looking for the dark eyes of my friend.

'Abdullah?' Perhaps he is in lessons now, as he should be. The sun is warm on my face and a floral scent has been picked up by the breeze. After a month inside, I close my eyes and savour the warmth. When I open them, I jump, he is standing right in front of me.

'Abdullah, my friend!' I go to throw my arms around him, but he steps back.

'Adisa said you thought I'd poisoned you? How could you think that? I would never do that. Not to you or anyone.'

'Abdullah, I…'

'Save it.' He turns to stalk away, but I pull him back, and I flinch in pain. His fury turns to concern.

'Are you ok?' He asks.

'Abdullah, we both know who it did, but Mr. Adisa doesn't believe me. He told me he doesn't trust you and he wants to protect me. I want him to learn to trust you, like I do.'

'I was so worried about you.'

'God's will brought me back.'

'Thank God.'

'I have something for you,' I hand him the thing I treasure more than anything, my Bible.

'Lela, isn't this your holy book? I can't take this from you.'

'Please, I want you to have it. I want it to do for you what it has done for me.'

'Thank you, thank you, I shall always treasure it.' He tucks it into the back of his trousers and smiles, then pulls me close to him in a warm embrace.

'I missed you, I was so worried about you, that you weren't going to make it.'

'I was never going to leave you alone, now was I?'

'We will see each other, won't we, even if Adisa won't allow it?'

'I will make sure of it.' I confirm, 'We can always meet out here. I had better go, before Adisa checks up on me. You should be in lessons too.'

'Yes boss.' We laugh. I have missed him.

'Well done, Lela. Your report cards this term shows exceptional development. You have improved in every area; your sponsors are going to be so proud of you.'

I take the report and put it in my satchel, which rests at my feet.

'Thank you, Mr. Adisa,' The end of the year is finally here, and I survived, just about. I am in his office. It is in better condition than most of the building. The windows seal properly for a start, and the walls have been painted a sky blue. I suspect he did it himself. I have been in this room a lot since the accident, or should I say 'incident.' He brings me here for extra tuition. He has kept his word. He has protected me and helped me with every lesson.

He rises from the desk between us.

'It will be strange not seeing you over the holidays, but I will look forward to your return, the Webbs have quite an adventure in store, I believe.'

'Really?'

'Hmm…' he seems distracted and glances out of the window as the first of the cars arrive to take their children home.

'Do you know what they have planned?' I ask, trying to draw his attention back.

'Sorry? No idea. Sorry I'm distracted.'

'Is everything okay?'

'Hmm, yes.' His attention is bought back to me. 'Of course, next year we will not have to look out quite so much for you.'

'What do you mean?' Maybe Kizza was leaving!

'Abdullah has been withdrawn from school.'

'Where has he gone?' I can't hide my shock.

'Why do you look so concerned, child? I told you we couldn't trust him.'

My heart is beating fast. Did they transfer him somewhere? To another school? He told me once where he lived, I think I can remember, it wasn't far, could I find him?

'His father phoned me this morning.'

His father is not an understanding man.

'It seems he has been up to some horrible mischief, and his father has removed him. He said he needed a stricter establishment. I quite agree.'

I wrack my brain for the name of his village. It is close by. If I left now, I could be back before the Webbs come and get me.

'Are you alright Lela, you look quite ill?'

'I'm sorry sir, I have to leave, I have to, to say goodbye to someone.'

'Lela!' Mr. Adisa calls after me, but I have fled his tiny office and am racing through the building, knocking past

251

students and the first of the parents as they embrace their children.

'I'm sorry,' I call behind me, but do not stop until, at last, I reach his village. I bend over, clutching at the stitch in my stomach. Suddenly aware that I have no idea where in the village he lives.

'You ok, *Habibi*?' says an old woman. She tilts her chin towards the sky.

'Abdullah, I need to find Abdullah,' I gasp.

'Ha! Which one?'

'Please, please help me.'

'Girl, you have come to the land of Abdullahs. There must be thirty in this village.'

'The one like me, in this uniform,' I point to the school colours.

'Oh, him! You don't want anything to do with him, the trouble that boy brings his father... he is long gone anyhow.'

'Gone?'

'He bought his Father too much shame, he was sent away.'

'Sent where?'

'You ask too many questions child, I do not know it all.' She shrugs her shoulders and picks up a broom, turning her back on me.

'Please,' I realise I sound desperate, but my heart hurts for my friend.

'I'm sorry girl, I do not know much else,' She turns back to me. 'All I know is he came home one night and there was a lot of shouting, all night at their house, we gathered, but could not make head nor tail of it. In the morning the boy was gone. His father said he had caused him too much heart ache and had been sent to live with another family member, cousin maybe? It is all I know. Ask for yourself, they live down there.'

I thank her, though I feel much has been left unanswered and slowly meander down the street towards his home. Men congregate outside the shops, smoking their shisha pipes, playing odd games. They watch me with vague interest, then turn back to what they are doing. Women sweep the floors; tiny children play in the dirt but there are no boys my age. I look for Abdullah's kind face. I know already that I will not approach his house, if he is no longer there, I do not wish to face his angry father. But inside me there is a feeling of emptiness. I pray to God that Abdullah will write to me at school, or I may never see him again.

Chapter Forty-Four

The Webbs are there waiting for me, wondering where I am. We drive through the familiar streets back to their beautiful home. The worry for my friend Abdullah eats away at my stomach.

I catch Mr. Webb eyeing me through the rear-view mirror, then he glances at his wife.

'Is everything all right, Lela? Where were you? You look very hot and bothered.'

'Everything is fine,' I say, then feel guilty for the lie. 'I was just saying goodbye to someone.' That last is, at least, the partial truth, I was certainly trying. Where is my friend? Is he safe?

'And how are you feeling now? Mr. Adisa said you were in the hospital sometime, if we had known it was so serious, we would have come to see you.'

'I am much better, thank you.' I smile weakly at Mr. Webb's reflection in the mirror.

As always, I am torn. I don't like to lie or keep things from them, but would they believe me if I told them the truth? Should I tell them about the bullying? Should I tell them about the spiked porridge? Is there even any point in telling them about Abdullah and his disappearance, given I do not even know where he is? The adults say the boy is trouble, will they believe me that he is not?

'Lela, you know you can talk to us if you need to. If you want to.'

Neither of them wish to push me. Mrs. Webb inspects the contents of her handbag, Mr. Webb focuses on the road ahead, passing through yet another bustling suburban sprawl.

'Can I think about it first?' I eventually say.

Mrs. Webb smiles and turns to squeeze my hand. 'Of course, dear.'

The dusty streets whizz by the window. In spite of myself, I am drawn to the infinite variety of Kampala. This city has thrown me so many challenges, each a part of my story, of the person I am to become. I send a prayer to God to keep Abdullah safe.

The usual smells drift through the gap in the window, the endless crowds selling fruit, veg, the delicious street food which would normally call to me. Yet today I see only the pain of my people. Yes, the brightly dressed women chat and laugh, but in the dirt, there are toddlers who cry, old women whose eyes are weary, begging for coins so they can eat today, babies who sicken like my tiny sister Elizabeth.

It is dusk before we drive up the familiar dusty track. The Webb's home is illuminated in the dying light, a windowpane catches the reflection of the sun before it dips below the horizon. The air, as always, is thick with floral scents. We are not a million miles from school but here, we may as well be, and I breathe freely for the first time in an age. The knot of tension in my stomach eases. I do not have to think about Kizza or Zuluka for a whole month.

There is a delicious smell coming from the kitchen. Mrs. Webb left dinner on the slow cooker, so it would be ready for us on our return.

The Webbs seem awkward and eye one another. I wonder if they have sensed my tension and suddenly have second thoughts about bringing me back. What would I prefer? Going back to Bwaise, or going back to school? For the first time ever, Bwaise is not immediately dismissed as the worst option. I am older now. I have more skills, more experience. I miss my family. Suddenly, everything is too much. I drop my bag and burst into sobs.

'Lela, Lela! What is it child?' Demands Mrs. Webb as she takes me in her arms.

'My friend, the school, Kizza...' I attempt.

'Oh sweetheart, it seems you need a rest, thank goodness you are back here.'

'But you're both so quiet, so different...I thought you had regrets?'

She laughs. 'Only because we have a surprise for you. 'Come on.' Mrs. Webb takes me by the arm and steers me along the hallway to the room that has been dubbed my own.

'See that small package on your bed? Go on, open it.

My room is just as I left it. The package is a small, brown envelope with cardboard backing. With a nudge of encouragement, I pick it up, examining it from all sides.

'Open it.' Mr. Webb directs, jovially.

I ease open the sticky flap. Immediately a group of papers falls onto the bed, all clipped together with a little document book attached to the front. The book is shiny, bound in navy leather, like the material of the car seats. In the centre a large golden coloured stamp illuminates from the dark cover. The words *Republic of Uganda Passport* catch my eye. I look up at the Webbs.

'In this envelope are all the documents you need to travel with us to England, Lela. We want to take you to visit our home. We want you to come and meet our daughters and our friends.

'I, I do not understand.' This is their home, isn't it?

'Lela, our real home is in England. Tomorrow, we will visit Beatrice and your Jaaja, then the following day, will you come to England with us?'

Of course, I had heard of England before.

'Don't you need to get on a plane and travel for hours?'

'Yes!' They laugh. 'We want to take you home and introduce you to our family. In time, maybe, give you an education, in England, teach you to become a professional, a nurse perhaps? Give you the chance for a proper future.

'Lela?'

'Oh, my goodness, you want me? You want to help me? More than you have done already?'

'We care for you Lela. We have seen your family often since you introduced us, and we want you to see them whenever is possible, but this trip to England is an adventure just for you.'

Even Mr. Webb has tears in his eyes. He is embarrassed, and mutters something about checking on dinner.

'England's err... a little chillier than Uganda,' says Mrs. Webb. 'I got you some new clothes for the trip. Warm ones. I'll show you after we've eaten.' She follows her husband out.

I stare at the passport. Such a beautiful little book. The binding reminds me of the little Bible I gave Abdullah. It does not seem coincidental that the book in my hand resembles the book I turned to for help. I kneel beside my bed.

257

'Thank you, God, thank you for standing by me, for loving me when no one else did and for giving me the opportunity to feel love again. And please, please help Abdullah.'

I have an England in my mind. Rolling hills and clean running rivers, all the homes perfectly pristine, like the Webb's. The chest of drawers is full of the clothes that Mrs. Webb spoke about. I finger the material of some pure white trousers and a matching blouse, thinking what a perfect outfit it would be to wear in England.

We have a lovely dinner, talking excitedly about our trip and after dinner, Mrs. Webb shows me all my new clothes. She laughs when I tell her I want to pack right away, so I swap the clothes in my suitcase to the new purchases, all except the pure white outfit which I drape over the wicker chair. Eventually, I slip my lightweight nightdress over my head and wriggle beneath the bedsheets. The lettering on the passport gleams under the bedside lamp beside me. I turn to look at the outfit again, gleaming white in the darkness. I imagine myself wearing it as we land in England. I imagine myself fitting in, no one looking at me as though I am different, no one judging me. It will be like paradise, I tell myself.

We have a happy visit with my family. The people of Bwaise do not think the Webbs are so strange now. Beatrice and Jaaja are still sick, but they are fed and no longer have to worry about where their next meal is coming from. Juliet is plump and happy. She and Mr. Webb are firm friends. Dembe is doing well at the new school. We cannot see Hope or Ada, so I write to them instead.

On the night before my departure, I cannot sleep. My mind plays a thousand tricks on me. I know I should switch the light off but then I might go into a deep sleep and not wake at dawn. I cannot allow that. Leaping out of bed I decide it is best if I do not sleep at all, and then I will not miss the Webbs leaving. What if I say or do something stupid in front of their English family or friends? I cannot bear the thought. I pull my nightshirt back over my head and toss it onto my suitcase to add to my packing. Instead I step tentatively into the white cotton trousers. The material is so soft that I put each leg through slowly and carefully, terrified I will tear the fabric and ruin its perfection. The blouse too, slips over my head as though it were made from feathers. At last I admire my reflection. Before I came here, I never knew anything could be this white.

The clock flashes five past ten. I am in for a long wait, but I will not allow myself to sleep. I will go to England.

Epilogue

'Please fasten your seatbelts in preparation for landing.'
The pilot's voice crackles over the intercom. Below me a
familiar landscape comes into view; one I have not seen for
many years. I tighten my sweating palms around the seat belt
buckle, ensuring it is correctly fastened, and eye the bag
specifically designed for airsickness in the seat pocket. I have
felt queasy since stepping on board. I close my eyes, and my
visit to the hospital replays itself in my head.

I am lying on a cold surgical day bed, icy instruments run
over my body as I stare at the whitewashed ceiling. The
doctor mutters to the nurse, I hear words that I can't believe.
'Promiscuous' 'Sexually active from a young age.' My throat
tightens and I sweat, profusely.

'You may sit up,' the doctor announces as he noisily snaps
off his latex gloves. A curtain is drawn around me as I am
allowed privacy to re-dress, a little silly given the intimacy of
his examination. Once dressed, I peer around the blue sheet.
He invites me to take a seat. The nurse taps noisily on a
nearby keyboard.

'Well, we can easily see the source of the discomfort,
there appears to be large sections of scar tissue internally,
stretching from the vagina area all the way to your womb.
I'm afraid to say the damage is somewhat extensive and I
believe it may well affect your ability to have children in the
future.'

The plane veers to the left as we enter a more rapid
decent and I open my eyes, the doctor's words still echoing
around my head. To rape me, rip away my childhood was an
unspeakable crime, unforgivable, but to render me incapable
of having a child of my own... I have no words for the
monstrous injustice he has inflicted on me. I left the clinic
and booked my flight. It should feel like a homecoming,
returning to the land of my birth, but I sweat, nauseated, and
panic eats away at my insides, but it is time, I am here. I have
come back to confront Mussa.

I collect my bag from the hold above my head. It is tiny, but I do not intend to stay long. Inside the pocket is a scrawled address on a crumpled sheet of paper. It hadn't been hard to find out where he lived. Dembe knew someone, who knew someone, always the way in Uganda, where everyone knows everyone else's business. I often wonder how they didn't know I was raped in the dead of night. I remember my lovely neighbour, Jaaja, now long dead. She knew, and comforted me, yet ultimately could do nothing. Perhaps others knew too.

I glide through arrivals, passport in hand. It is Ugandan, so I am not questioned, and I am grateful. I have just one task. I need it done, and I need to be out of here.

Abdullah, with his face deeply scarred, comes into view as the swinging doors flap open. He greets me with a warm smile, and although my heart bursts with gratitude at seeing his familiar face once more, I cannot reciprocate his smile. I allow him to envelop me in his arms, his warm embrace is comforting, but my stomach continues to flutter with nerves.

'Ready?' his eyes lock with mine. I nod, just once. He collects my small travel bag and guides me through the terminal to his ancient Volvo, parked some distance from the airport buildings. It is the first time I have stepped on Ugandan soil for years, but I barely notice the smell as the sun hits the rich earth, nor the old sounds.

We meander our way through the crowded roads of Entebbe. Abdullah knows my mission, and spares me any small talk, the mark of a true friend.

'Have you thought of what you're going to say?' he asks.

I have done nothing but think about what I will say since I booked my ticket after my devastating trip to the clinic. Thinking rarely helps. 'Not really,' I admit.

'The words will come to you when you need them.'

The streets are as busy as they always were, and I have landed during rush hour. We swelter in the car, and it's an hour before we begin to move more freely. My palms sweat all the time and I wonder if I need the toilet, but I have strong memories of the public latrines and cross my legs.

'Lela, we are nearly there.' Abdullah pulls me from my thoughts. I straighten in my seat, my eyes focus on where he points, 'Just up ahead.'

He weaves in and out of children playing, then slows to a stop.

'Is this it?' I ask looking around.

'Almost, just around the corner. Are you ready? Do you really want to do this?'

'It is not something I want to do. I *need* to do it. If I don't, I can't carry on with my life. I will never get married; I might never be able to have children.' I cannot tell him that I have never been able to be in a romantic relationship, let alone a sexual one. The memory of Mussa has held me back every time I meet someone. The latest disaster, the Minister's son, comes to mind. I felt dishonest keeping my dirty secret from someone who wanted a future with me. He dropped my hand as though I were a leper. His subsequent excuses were laughably lame. I could go on. I could tell Abdullah that all these years I have felt as though it were my fault, that I should have fought back, should have kept a knife by my bed, should have told Taata, should have escaped sooner. Strangely, the clinic visit has freed me from that guilt, replacing it with a furious, seething anger. 'Promiscuous.' 'Sexually active from a young age.' As if I had *chosen* to be attacked, defiled, abused, degraded? I need to move on with my life.

Abdullah sees my need to persevere regardless and puts the car back into gear. We coast around the corner. We are in a semi-affluent area, not Bwaise, no slums here. Terraced houses, but with stable walls and sturdy roofs. The car stops again and Abdullah nods to confirm we have arrived. Opposite, little girls dart in and out of a house chasing one another, a man watching over them. My heart sinks to the pit of my stomach. So much time has passed but I could never forget his lazy stance, his slumped shoulders. Abdullah and I climb from the car into the warm sunshine. Though the change in light surprises me I do not remove my gaze from Mussa. Abdullah walks ahead.

'You are Mussa?' He demands.

'I am,' His voice is deeper than it was, raspier, I suspect he has taken to smoking profusely, but it is unmistakably him. The anger seizes me violently and I stride forward regardless.

'Do you remember me?' I challenge. He shows no sign of recognition. The urgency in my voice has halted the girls' play and they look to the hysterical woman.

'Taata?' One begins, and my stomach is sick. Taata. The beast has given birth to daughters. Four beautiful, innocent faces glance up at their father, faces full of trust. A woman too, steps into the sunlight. It might be a moment for discretion, but I cannot stop myself now I have started.

'Look at me, look at my face, how can you not remember me?' The woman anticipates trouble and motions to her daughters, shepherding them into the darkness of the house, while she steps forward to join the monster.

'It is me, Lela. The child you raped. I was no older than these girls, your girls!' My fists are clenched, and, in my head, I am beating him, he so richly deserves it, but my feet are glued to one spot. I had imagined this moment so many times, but the reality is very different. For the lifetime of suffering he inflicted on me, my stolen childhood, his fate should have been altered. And yet I find him here, in a peaceful home, with beautiful children and a loving wife. The injustice burns.

He does not move; his eyes hold my glare.

'Look at me. I have made something of my life.' To my horror I feel my tears spill. I fight them, I wanted to be so strong, but they fall on their own accord, I have no control. Through clenched teeth I continue, 'I have friends, family, education, I am a graduate with a degree, but what you did to me stays with me every moment of my life. What if someone did this to your daughters, those lovely little girls, what would *you* do? You would kill them with your bare hands. That's what I want to do to you,' I snarl.

Still nothing. He just stares, he does not move, he barely blinks. I cannot read his features, I see no guilt, no remorse, a blank canvas. I could stand here forever, and I suspect an apology would never come.

One of the girls rushes out of the house. She points furiously at me. 'Why are you shouting at my Taata?'

I look at her lovely little face, her beautiful brown eyes. I take her chin into my hand and gently lift it. 'I am telling him to keep you safe.'

In that second, I feel the anger evaporate. I look back to Mussa, his eyes watching me touch his child. 'I am not here to shout, I have grown up,' I do not avert my gaze as I speak, slower and steadier now, 'I will waste no more tears on you. I am here to pass the baton, this burden is no longer mine to carry, it is now yours, I am done with it… it is time for me to be free.'

Abdullah takes my arm and steers me towards the car. We both know I will never receive the simple sorry I warrant. I continue to stare at Mussa. When I am back in the car, Mussa turns away and goes back into the house, his wife following obediently behind.

We drive off and Abdullah passes me a tissue as I am crying uncontrollably. I mop my eyes and nose before sitting up to catch my breath.

When we're out of sight, he stops the car and turns to me in concern. I think he is amazed to see that I am smiling through my tears. Mussa now knows that he didn't break me, that I am stronger than he will ever be. He *saw* me, he *heard* me. his *wife* heard me, and he will have to live with that for the rest of his days. As for me, I can breathe again, released to carry on with my life, whatever it has in store for me.

Dedications

From Lela

It would be impossible to mention everyone that has walked with me along the way but, please, know that I am grateful to you all. For welcoming me into your lives, opening your homes to me and for sharing all that you have with me. It is because of your kindness and generosity that I share my memories, as a token of my thanks.

My sincere gratitude to my family, especially my dear husband Andrew. I thank God every day for giving you to me. Thank you for accepting me as I am, for being patient and supportive. To my children; having you has been the miracle I needed to heal, I will forever celebrate you.

To my siblings, thank you for giving me purpose, a reason not to give up on life and for keeping me focused.

To my parents-in-law Mark and Kathie, thank you for always being present, supportive and for enduring to read the book in its early stages.

To Mike, Marrietta, Lore and Nadine. I am forever grateful that you opened your home and welcomed me, a stranger, into your lives.

Carly West, there are no words to express how grateful I am to have you in my life. Thank you for always seeing the best in me.

Tamsin Prout, thank you for starting me on this beautiful journey with your kindness and generosity.

Kerry and Charles Hine, thank you for believing in me at a time when I felt helpless.

Martha and Fraser Lindsay, I am glad we met at the cheese market on that cold day. Thank you for encouraging me not to give up and for always praying for and with us.

To my co-Author Sarah Jarman, this book would not have happened without you. Thank you for being so understanding, for not judging me and for accepting to carry the burden of my story. Your hard work is evident, and I am forever indebted.

Cathy Evans, what can I say, you inspire me in so many ways. Thank you for sharing your expertise and your great sense of humour with us.

Juliet Dobson, for your proof-reading skills and for picking up on the mistakes we missed!

To all those of you that have taken the time to read my story thus far, I am so grateful to you. My story is not yet over, I hope you will stay with me on this journey.

And finally, a big thank you to God Almighty for giving me life and the big family I belong to all over the world.

From Sarah

To be trusted, by Lela, with her incredible story, is an overwhelming honour. I know how hard it was for you, Lela, to bring so many of these memories back to the surface and I only hope I have given it the justice it deserves. Writing this book has been an emotional process, and, while we were friends before, I now feel we have bonded immeasurably. Thank you for making me a part of your life.

Writing Lela – Ashes of Childhood has been very emotive, and I want to thank my husband and children for standing by me throughout the process. I realise there were a lot of late nights, tears and weekends eaten up by working: I can't have been easy to live with. I am so grateful that you continued to believe in me and helped me make it to the end.

My writing journey would never have begun without the support of my parents, stepparents and siblings. You encouraged me from the second I voiced my hopes of becoming an author, all through school and university and taught me to never give up on my dreams.

A massive thank you goes to Cathy Evans for helping us to 'fine-tune' the story and make it what it is today.

Finally, I would like to thank my friends; Lisa, Jenni, Jodie, Kath, Sam, Ellie and Emma for all the late night 'whatsapping'. Helping to motivate me, amuse me and correct me on occasion!

About the Authors

Lela Burbridge is a Writer, Speaker and an advocate for education for all. She grew up in Kampala, Uganda. Despite tough beginnings Lela moved to the United Kingdom to further her education. She holds a Degree in Health and Social Care and a Master's in Public Health from the University of Essex. She now lives in the Cotswolds with her children and husband, Andrew. Lela and Andrew run a business together.

Sarah Jarman is a Writer, Artist and Jeweller. Originally from Britain, she grew up in the Middle East and returned to England to study Creative Writing and English Studies at Bath Spa University. Sarah went on to follow a career in Jewellery, gaining further jewellery qualifications. After having children, Sarah set up her own business as a Freelance Writer, Blogger and Artist, selling products from her online portfolio. She lives with her husband and two children in the Cotswolds.